PHILIP'S BRITAIN & IRELAND

2021 STARGAZING

MONTH-BY-MONTH GUIDE TO THE NIGHT SKY

HEATHER COUPER & NIGEL HENBEST

www.philipsastronomy.com
www.philips-maps.co.uk

Published in Great Britain in 2020 by Philip's,
a division of Octopus Publishing Group Limited
(www.octopusbooks.co.uk)
Carmelite House, 50 Victoria Embankment,
London EC4Y 0DZ
An Hachette UK Company (www.hachette.co.uk)

TEXT
Heather Couper and Nigel Henbest © 2020 pp. 4–85
CPRE © 2017 pp. 90–91
Philip's © 2020 pp. 1–3
Robin Scagell © 2020 pp. 86–89

MAPS
pp. 92–95 © OpenStreetMap contributors, Earth
Observation Group, NOAA National Geophysical Data
Center. Developed by CPRE and LUC.

ARTWORKS © Philip's

ISBN 978-1-84907-541-1

Printed in China

Title page: Dancing aurora display in Iceland.

CONTENTS

Welcome to this year's freshly revised edition of *Stargazing*! Within these pages, you'll find your complete guide to everything that's happening in the night sky throughout 2021 – whether you're a beginner or an experienced astronomer.

With the 12 monthly Star Charts, you can find your way around the sky on any night in the year. Impress your friends by identifying celestial sights ranging from the brightest planets to some pretty obscure constellations.

Every page of the *2021 Stargazing* guide is bang up-to-date, bringing you everything that's new this year, from shooting stars to eclipses. And we'll start with a run-down of the most exciting sky sights on view in 2021 (see opposite).

THE MONTHLY CHARTS

A reliable map is just as essential for exploring the heavens as it is for visiting a foreign country. For each month, we provide a circular **Star Chart** showing the whole evening sky.

To keep the maps uncluttered, we've plotted about 200 of the brighter stars (down to third magnitude), which means you can pick out the main star patterns – the constellations. (If we'd shown every star visible on a really dark night, there'd be around 3000 stars on the charts!) We also show the ecliptic: the apparent path of the Sun in the sky; it's closely followed by the Moon and planets as well.

You can use the charts throughout the UK and Ireland, along with most of Europe, North America and northern Asia – between 40 and 60 degrees north – though our detailed timings apply specifically to the UK and Ireland.

USING THE STAR CHARTS

It's pretty easy to use the charts. Start by working out roughly your compass points. South is where the Sun is highest in the sky during the day, east is roughly where the Sun rises, and west where it sets. At night, you can find north by locating the Pole Star – Polaris – by using the stars of the Plough (see March's Constellation).

The left-hand chart then shows your view to the north. Most of these stars are visible all year: the circumpolar constellations wheel around Polaris as the seasons progress. Your view to the south appears in the right-hand chart; it changes much more as the Earth orbits the Sun. Leo's prominent 'sickle' is high in the spring skies. Summer is dominated by the bright trio of Vega, Deneb and Altair. Autumn's familiar marker is the Square of Pegasus, while the stars of Orion rule the winter sky.

During the night, our perspective on the sky alters as the Earth spins around, making the stars and planets appear to rise in the east and set in the west. The charts depict the sky in the late evening (the exact times are noted in the captions). As a rule of thumb, if you are observing two hours later, then the following month's map will be a better guide to the stars on view – though beware: the Moon and planets won't be in the right place!

THE PLANETS, MOON AND SPECIAL EVENTS

Our charts also highlight the **planets** above the horizon in the late evening.

HIGHLIGHTS OF THE YEAR

- **Night of 3/4 January:** the maximum of the Quadrantid meteor shower, although this year the display is spoilt by bright moonlight.
- **14 January:** the crescent Moon lies to the left of Mercury, Jupiter and Saturn.
- **21 January:** Mars travels past Uranus.
- **18 and 19 February:** the crescent Moon joins Mars near the Pleiades.
- **3 March:** Mars passes below the Pleiades.
- **5 March (am):** Mercury very close to Jupiter.
- **19 March:** the Moon lies very near to Mars, in the vicinity of the Pleiades, Aldebaran and the Hyades.
- **6 and 7 April (am):** you'll find the crescent Moon near Saturn and Jupiter.
- **16 April:** the Moon lies between Aldebaran (below) and Mars (above).
- **17 April:** Mars is next to the Moon.
- **25 April:** Mercury lies just to the right of Venus.
- **4 May:** Mercury passes to the left of the Pleiades, with Venus below.
- **Night of 5/6 May:** maximum of the Eta Aquarid meteor shower.
- **13 May:** to the upper left of Venus you'll find the crescent Moon adjacent to Mercury.
- **26 May:** the biggest and brightest Full Moon of 2021, just 357,314 kilometres from the Earth.
- **10 June:** we are treated to a partial solar eclipse, with the Sun 20 per cent obscured as seen from London and 32 per cent from Glasgow. Regions of northern Canada and eastern Siberia experience an annular eclipse.
- **13 June:** Mars is next to the Moon, with Venus to the lower right.
- **23 June:** Mars passes in front of Praesepe.
- **2 and 3 July:** Venus grazes the fringes of Praesepe.
- **12 July:** Venus and Mars appear very close together, just below the crescent Moon.
- **2 August:** Saturn is opposite to the Sun in the sky, and closest to the Earth
- **10 August:** the Moon lies between Venus and the fainter trio of Mercury, Mars and Regulus.
- **11 August:** a beautiful spectacle of the crescent Moon with Venus.
- **Night of 12/13 August:** maximum of the Perseid meteor shower, putting on an excellent display this year.
- **20 August:** Jupiter is at its nearest this year and opposite to the Sun in the sky.
- **10 September:** Venus forms a stunning duo with the crescent Moon.
- **14 September:** Neptune is opposite to the Sun in the sky and at its closest to the Earth.
- **9 October:** a glorious tableau of the crescent Moon and Venus, near Antares.
- **15 October:** the brilliant 'star' near the Moon is Jupiter.
- **29 October:** Venus reaches its maximum eastern elongation.
- **5 November:** Uranus is opposite to the Sun in the sky and at its closest to the Earth.
- **8 November:** the crescent Moon is near Venus.
- **10 November (am):** Mercury glides to the left of Mars, with Spica to the upper right.
- **7 December:** Venus peaks in brightness (magnitude –4.7), next to the crescent Moon.
- **8 December:** the Moon hangs between Venus and Jupiter, below fainter Saturn.
- **Night of 13/14 December:** your best views of the Geminid meteor shower will come after midnight, when the Moon has set.

We've indicated the track of any **comets** known at the time of writing; though we're afraid we can't guide you to a comet that's found after the book has been printed!

We've plotted the position of the Full Moon each month, and also the **Moon's position** at three-day intervals before and after the Full Moon. If there's a meteor shower in the month, we mark its radiant – the position from which the meteors stream.

The **Calendar** provides a daily guide to the Moon's phases and other celestial happenings. We've detailed the most interesting in the **Special Events** section, including close pairings of the planets, times of the equinoxes and solstices and – most exciting – **eclipses** of the Moon and Sun.

Check out the **Planet Watch** page for more about the other worlds of the Solar System, including their antics at times they're not on the main monthly charts. We've illustrated unusual planetary and lunar goings-on in the **Planet Event Charts**. And there's a full explanation of all these events in **Solar System 2021** on pp. 80–82.

MONTHLY OBJECTS, TOPICS AND PICTURES

Each month, we examine one particularly interesting **Object**: a planet, a star or a galaxy. We also feature a spectacular **Picture** – taken by an amateur based in Britain – describing how the image was captured, and subsequently processed to enhance the end result. And we explore a fascinating and often newsworthy **Topic**, ranging from Supermoons to the Big Bang.

GETTING IN DEEP

There's a practical **Observing Tip** each month, helping you to explore the sky with the naked eye, binoculars or a telescope.

Check out our guide to the **Top 20 Sky Sights**, such as nebulae, star clusters and galaxies. You'll find it on pp. 83–85.

It's followed by equipment expert **Robin Scagell's article** on the fascinating astronomy you can undertake with binoculars – including in-depth advice on how to choose the best pair.

If you're plagued by light pollution, use the **Dark-sky Maps** (pp. 90–95). They show you where to find the blackest skies in Great Britain, and enjoy the most breathtaking views of the heavens.

So: fingers crossed for good weather, beautiful planets, a multitude of meteors and – the occasional surprise.

Happy stargazing!

JARGON BUSTER

Have you ever wondered how astronomers describe the brightness of the stars or how far apart they appear in the sky? Not to mention how we can measure the distances to the stars? If so, you can quickly find yourself mired in some arcane astro-speak – magnitudes, arcminutes, light years and the like.

Here's our quick and easy guide to busting that jargon:

Magnitudes
It only takes a glance at the sky to see that some stars are pretty brilliant, while many more are dim. But how do we describe to other people how bright a star appears?

Around 2000 years ago, ancient Greek astronomers ranked the stars into six classes, or **magnitudes**, depending on their brightness. The most brilliant stars were first

magnitude, and the faintest stars you can see came in at sixth magnitude. So the stars of the Plough, for instance, are second magnitude while the individual Seven Sisters in the Pleiades are fourth magnitude.

Mars (magnitude –1.6 here) shines a hundred times brighter than the Seven Sisters in the Pleiades, which are around 5 magnitudes fainter.

Today, scientists can measure the light from the stars with amazing accuracy. (Mathematically speaking, a difference of five magnitudes represents a difference in brightness of one hundred times.) So the Pole Star is magnitude +2.0, while Rigel is magnitude +0.1. Because we've inherited the ancient ranking system, the brightest stars have the *smallest* magnitude. In fact, the most brilliant stars come in with a negative magnitude, including Sirius (magnitude –1.5).

And we can use the magnitude system to describe the brightness of other objects in the sky, such as stunning Venus, which can be almost as brilliant as magnitude –5. The Full Moon and the Sun have whopping negative magnitudes!

At the other end of the scale, stars, nebulae and galaxies with a magnitude fainter than +6.5 are too dim to be seen by the naked eye. Using ever larger telescopes – or by observing from above Earth's atmosphere – you can perceive fainter and fainter objects. The most distant galaxies visible to the Hubble Space Telescope are ten billion times fainter than the naked-eye limit.

Here's a guide to the magnitude of some interesting objects:

Sun	–26.7
Full Moon	–12.5
Venus (at its brightest)	–4.7
Sirius	–1.5
Betelgeuse	+0.4
Polaris (Pole Star)	+2.0
Faintest star visible to the naked eye	+6.5
Faintest star visible to the Hubble Space Telescope	+31

Degrees of separation

Astronomers measure the distance between objects in the sky in **degrees** (symbol °): all around the horizon is 360°, while it's 90° from the horizon to the point directly overhead (the zenith).

As we show in the photograph, you can use your hand – held at arm's length – to give a rough idea of angular distances in the sky.

For objects that are very close together – like many double stars – we divide the degree into 60 arcminutes (symbol '). And for celestial objects that are very tiny – such as the discs of the planets – we split each arcminute into 60 arcseconds (symbol "). To give you an idea of how small these units are, it takes 3600 arcseconds to make up one degree.

Here are some typical separations and sizes in the sky:

Length of the Plough	25°
Width of Orion's Belt	3°
Diameter of the Moon	31'
Separation of Mizar and Alcor	12'
Diameter of Jupiter	45"
Separation of Albireo A and B	35"

How far's that star?

Everything we see in the heavens lies a long way off. We can give distances to the planets in millions of kilometres. But the stars are so distant that even the nearest, Proxima Centauri, lies some 40 million million kilometres away. To turn those distances into something more manageable, astronomers use a larger unit: one **light year** is the distance that light travels in a year.

One light year is about 9.46 million million kilometres. That makes Proxima Centauri a much more manageable 4.2 light years away from us. Here are the distances to some other familiar astronomical objects, in light years:

Sirius	8.6
Betelgeuse	720
Centre of the Milky Way	26,000
Andromeda Galaxy	2.5 million
Most distant galaxies seen by the Hubble Space Telescope	13 billion

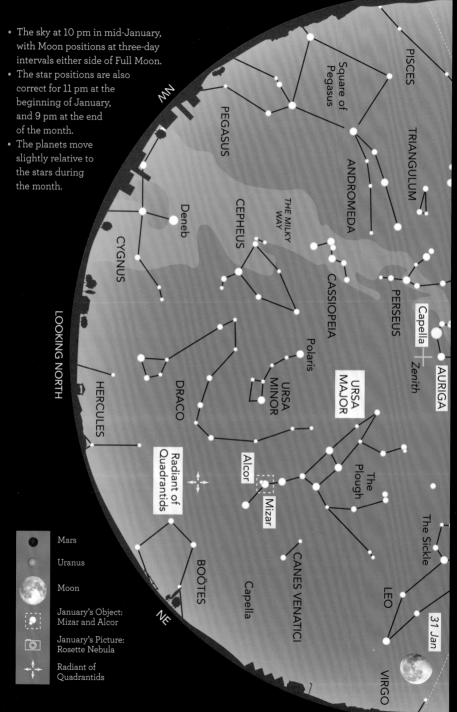

- The sky at 10 pm in mid-January, with Moon positions at three-day intervals either side of Full Moon.
- The star positions are also correct for 11 pm at the beginning of January, and 9 pm at the end of the month.
- The planets move slightly relative to the stars during the month.

WEST

PISCES

Square of Pegasus

TRIANGULUM

PEGASUS

ANDROMEDA

Deneb

THE MILKY WAY

CEPHEUS

CYGNUS

CASSIOPEIA

PERSEUS

Capella

Zenith

AURIGA

LOOKING NORTH

HERCULES

DRACO

Polaris

URSA MINOR

URSA MAJOR

Radiant of Quadrantids

Alcor

The Plough

The Sickle

Mizar

BOÖTES

Capella

CANES VENATICI

LEO

31 Jan

NE

VIRGO

Mars

Uranus

Moon

January's Object: Mizar and Alcor

January's Picture: Rosette Nebula

Radiant of Quadrantids

8   JANUARY

EAST

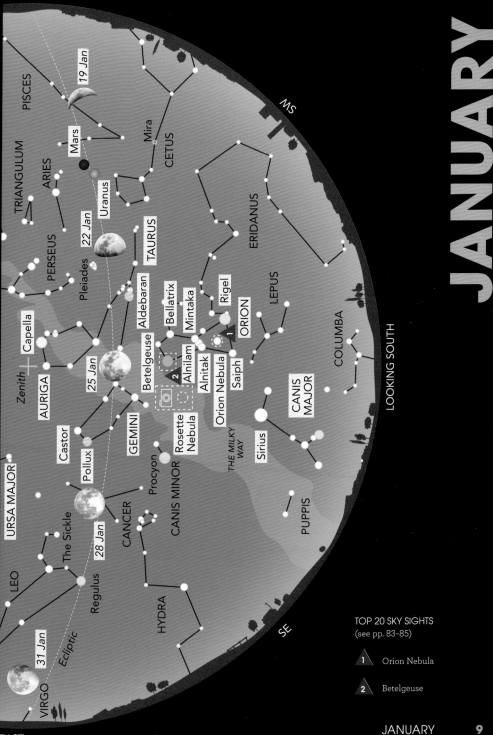

WEST

PISCES
19 Jan
TRIANGULUM
Mars
ARIES
Mira
Uranus
CETUS
22 Jan
PERSEUS
Pleiades
TAURUS
Aldebaran
ERIDANUS
Bellatrix
Mintaka
Rigel
Betelgeuse
ORION
LEPUS
Zenith
Capella
25 Jan
AURIGA
Alnilam
Alnitak
Orion Nebula
Saiph
COLUMBA
Castor
GEMINI
Rosette
Nebula
CANIS
MAJOR
URSA MAJOR
Pollux
Procyon
THE MILKY
WAY
Sirius
The Sickle
28 Jan
CANCER
CANIS MINOR
LEO
Regulus
PUPPIS
31 Jan
HYDRA
Ecliptic
VIRGO

EAST

W

S

LOOKING SOUTH

SE

TOP 20 SKY SIGHTS
(see pp. 83–85)

1 Orion Nebula

2 Betelgeuse

JANUARY

The year starts out with a dazzling cast of the sky's leading celebrity stars. **Betelgeuse** and **Rigel** blaze in the hunter **Orion**, with glorious **Sirius** in **Canis Major** (the Great Dog) to the lower left. Forming a giant arc above, you'll find **Aldebaran**, the bright red eye of **Taurus** (the Bull); **Capella**, crowning **Auriga** (the Charioteer); and **Castor** and **Pollux**, the celestial twins in **Gemini**. **Mars** heads up the planetary display, with Jupiter, Saturn and Mercury low in the evening twilight.

JANUARY'S CONSTELLATION

Spectacular **Orion** is a rare star grouping that looks like its namesake – a giant hunter with a sword below his belt, wielding a club. The seven main stars lie in the 'Top 70' brightest stars in the sky, but they're not closely associated – they simply line up, one behind the other.

Closest – at 250 light years – is the fainter of the two stars forming the hunter's shoulders, **Bellatrix**. The other shoulder-star, blood-red **Betelgeuse**, lies 720 light years away. This giant star is a thousand times larger than our Sun, and its fate will be to explode as a supernova (see February's Object).

Slightly brighter, blue-white **Rigel** (Orion's foot) – 860 light years from us – is a young star twice as hot as our Sun, and 125,000 times more luminous. **Saiph**, the hunter's other foot, is 650 light years distant.

We must travel around 1300 light years from home to reach the stars of Orion's glittering belt – **Alnitak, Alnilam** and **Mintaka** – and the great **Orion Nebula**. The nearest massive star factory, the Orion Nebula contains hundreds of embryonic stars, in many cases surrounded by a dusty disc that's poised to form into a system of planets.

JANUARY'S OBJECT

Home in on the 'kink' in the tail of **Ursa Major** (the Great Bear), and you'll spot the most famous pair of stars in the sky – **Mizar** (magnitude +2.0) and **Alcor** (magnitude +4.0). Generations of astronomers have referred to them as 'the horse and rider', and many books say they are orbiting each other.

But *are* Mizar and Alcor an item: perhaps Alcor just happens to lie in front of Mizar? This subject has been a bone of contention between astronomers for decades. The most recent measurements, however, put them at very much the same distance from us: 82 light years for Alcor and 83 for Mizar, so they are almost certainly in a gravitational embrace.

OBSERVING TIP

If you want to stargaze at this most glorious time of year, dress up warmly! Lots of layers are better than just a heavy coat, as they trap more air close to your skin, while heavy-soled boots with two pairs of socks stop the frost creeping up your legs. It may sound anorak-ish, but a woolly hat prevents a lot of your body heat escaping through the top of your head. And – alas – no hipflask of whisky. Alcohol constricts the veins, and makes you feel even colder.

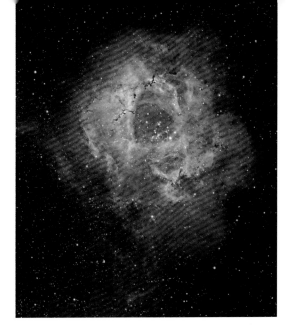

Jean Dean imaged the Rosette with a Starlight Xpress Trius 814 CCD camera, on a 60-mm Takahashi FS-60CB apochromatic refractor, at La Société Guernesiaise Astronomical Observatory, Guernsey. She took exposures through a set of filters (LRGB, H-alpha, SII and OIII), for a total exposure time of 13 hours.

But it's not a simple double star system. Mizar has a companion that's visible through a telescope, and both these stars are actually double, making four stars in all. And Alcor has a very faint companion, too – so there's a total of six stars making up this amazing system.

JANUARY'S TOPIC: TYCHO BRAHE

Tycho Brahe (1546–1601) was unique. A colourful Danish aristocrat, he lived in a magnificent castle and boasted a 'golden' nose – to replace one cut off in a duel. (It later turned out to be largely copper.) Owner of a pet elk, Tycho got it drunk one night; the poor creature fell down stairs and died.

He also designed and built the most astonishing collection of astronomical measuring equipment in the world. Funded by the king of Denmark (to an amount substantially more than NASA's share of the US budget today), Tycho mapped the skies more rigorously than anyone before. His quest? To prove Nicolaus Copernicus right or wrong: did the Earth circle the Sun, or the Sun orbit the Earth?

When the Danish king died, Tycho headed off for Prague to find a new sponsor. There he met German mathematician Johannes Kepler (1571–1630), who couldn't have been more different from Tycho – introverted, hypochondriac and depressive.

Yet the two made a brilliant team. Tycho provided Kepler with his observations; Kepler analysed them meticulously. Together, they would draw up a blueprint of the Solar System's architecture – with the Sun at the centre.

All that was now needed was the invention of the telescope. . .

JANUARY'S PICTURE

The glorious **Rosette Nebula** is a true celestial gem, imaged here by Jean Dean in a stunning picture that made newspaper headlines in 2019. Some 5000 light years away, the petals of the rose spread out over 130 light years of space. Baby stars are being born in the nebula today, their violent radiation and winds punching a hole in the nebula's heart. Researchers calculate that the Rosette is capable of giving birth to 10,000 stars.

JANUARY'S CALENDAR

SUNDAY	MONDAY	TUESDAY	WEDNESDAY	THURSDAY	FRIDAY	SATURDAY
31					1 Moon near Praesepe (am)	2 Earth at perihelion; Moon near Regulus
3 Quadrantids	4 Quadrantids (am)	5	6 9.37 am Last Quarter Moon	7 Moon near Spica (am)	8	9
10 Moon near Antares (am)	11 Crescent Moon near Venus (am)	12	13 5.00 am New Moon	14 Crescent Moon near Mercury, Jupiter and Saturn	15	16
17	18	19	20 9.01 pm First Quarter Moon near Mars	21 Mars close to Uranus, with the Moon nearby	22 Moon near the Pleiades	23 Moon between the Pleiades and Aldebaran/the Hyades
24 Mercury E elongation	25	26	27 Moon near Castor and Pollux	28 Moon near Praesepe; 7.16 pm Full Moon	29 Moon near Regulus	30

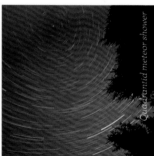

SPECIAL EVENTS

- **2 January, 1.50 pm:** the Earth is at perihelion, its closest point to the Sun (147 million km away).
- **Night of 3/4 January:** the maximum of the annual **Quadrantid meteor shower**, dust particles from the old comet 2003 EH$_1$ burning up in the Earth's atmosphere.

It's one of most prolific meteor showers, but this year the display is spoilt by bright moonlight.

- **11 January, 8 am:** catch a lovely pairing of Venus with the thinnest crescent Moon in the south-east, just before dawn.
- **14 January 4.30 pm:** low in the twilight to the south-west,

the new crescent Moon lies to the left of Mercury, Jupiter and Saturn (Chart 1a). Use binoculars to more easily spot the planets and Moon against the sunset glow.

- **21 January:** Mars passes above Uranus (see Planet Watch and Chart 1b).

Quadrantid meteor shower

1a *14 January, 4.30 pm. The crescent Moon with Mercury, Jupiter and Saturn.*

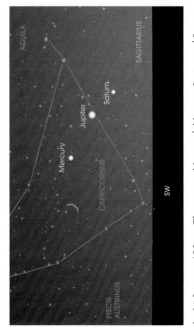

1b *21 January, 8 pm. Mars close to Uranus, next to the Moon.*

• At the start of January, **Mars** is brighter than any of the stars apart from Sirius, at magnitude –0.2. During the month, it fades as Earth pulls away: by the close of January, Mars has dropped to magnitude +0.4. Moving rapidly from Pisces to Aries, the planet sinks below the horizon around 1.45 am.

• On 21 January, the Red Planet lies near **Uranus** (Chart 1b). You'll find the seventh planet 1.5° to the lower left of Mars, on the verge of raked-eye visibility at magnitude +5.8 but best seen in binoculars. Setting about 1.45 am, Uranus lies in Aries.

• At the beginning of the month, giant planet **Jupiter** is very low in the south-western twilight after sunset and shining at magnitude –1.9. The Solar System's second largest world, **Saturn**, lies to its lower right, ten times fainter at magnitude +0.6. Both planets are in Capricornus and set around 5.45 pm.

• **Mercury** steams up from the sunset horizon early in January: the innermost planet is at magnitude –0.9 on 11 January when it passes below Jupiter. On 14 January, there's a lovely tableau of Mercury, Jupiter and Saturn with the crescent Moon (Chart 1a). Mercury is at its maximum separation from the Sun on 24 January. By the end of the month, Mercury has faded to magnitude +1.0, but is visible in a darker sky as it doesn't set until 6.15 pm.

• **Neptune**, at magnitude +7.9 visible only in binoculars or a telescope, lies in Aquarius and sets about 9.15 pm.

• At the start of January, you can't miss magnificent **Venus** in the dawn sky. Low in the south-east, the Morning Star blazes at magnitude –3.9, and rises around 6.30 am. But it's sinking down into the twilight, and has disappeared from sight by the end of the month.

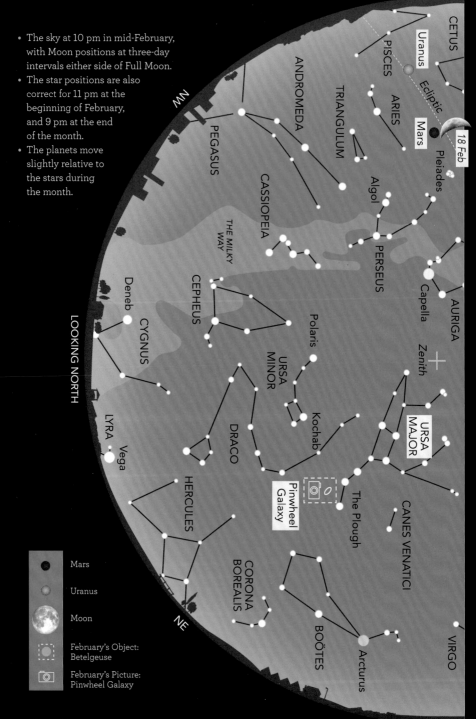

- The sky at 10 pm in mid-February, with Moon positions at three-day intervals either side of Full Moon.
- The star positions are also correct for 11 pm at the beginning of February, and 9 pm at the end of the month.
- The planets move slightly relative to the stars during the month.

WEST

CETUS

PISCES

Uranus

Ecliptic

ARIES

Mars

18 Feb

Pleiades

Algol

ANDROMEDA

TRIANGULUM

NW

PEGASUS

CASSIOPEIA

PERSEUS

THE MILKY WAY

Capella

AURIGA

CEPHEUS

Deneb

CYGNUS

Polaris

Zenith

LOOKING NORTH

URSA MINOR

Kochab

URSA MAJOR

LYRA

Vega

DRACO

Pinwheel Galaxy

The Plough

CANES VENATICI

HERCULES

CORONA BOREALIS

BOÖTES

VIRGO

NE

Arcturus

EAST

Mars

Uranus

Moon

February's Object: Betelgeuse

February's Picture: Pinwheel Galaxy

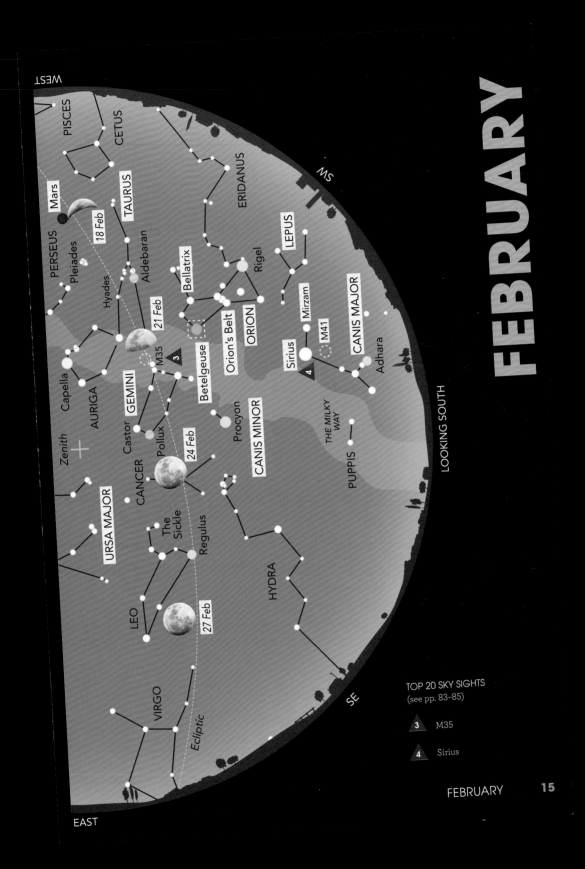

FEBRUARY

WEST

PISCES

CETUS

Mars

PERSEUS

TAURUS

18 Feb

Pleiades

Hyades

Aldebaran

ERIDANUS

Bellatrix

Rigel

LEPUS

21 Feb

Orion's Belt

ORION

Mirzam

M35

Betelgeuse

Sirius

M41

CANIS MAJOR

Adhara

Capella

Zenith

AURIGA

GEMINI

Castor

Procyon

Pollux

CANIS MINOR

24 Feb

THE MILKY
WAY

URSA MAJOR

CANCER

The
Sickle

Regulus

PUPPIS

LEO

27 Feb

HYDRA

VIRGO

Ecliptic

EAST

SW

LOOKING SOUTH

SE

3

4

The winter star patterns – **Orion, Taurus** and **Gemini** – are drifting westward, as a result of our annual orbit around the Sun. Imagine: you're whirling round on a fairground carousel, and looking out around you. At times you spot the ghost train, sometimes you see the roller-coaster, and then you swing past the candy-floss stall. So it is with the sky: as we circle our local star, we get to see different stars and constellations with the changing seasons.

FEBRUARY'S CONSTELLATION

Crowned by **Sirius**, the brightest star in the sky, **Canis Major** is the larger of Orion's two hunting dogs. He is represented as chasing **Lepus**, the Hare – a very faint constellation below Orion – but his main quarry is **Taurus**, the Bull. Take a line from Sirius through **Orion's Belt,** and you'll spot the celestial bovine on the other side.

Arabian astronomers accorded great importance to Canis Major, while the Indians regarded both cosmic dogs (**Canis Minor** lies to the left of Orion) as being 'watchdogs of the Milky Way', which runs between the two constellations.

To the right of Sirius is the star **Mirzam**. Its Arabic name means 'the Announcer', because the presence of Mirzam heralded the appearance of Sirius, one of the heaven's most venerated stars. Just below Sirius is the beautiful star cluster **M41**. This lovely grouping of around a hundred young stars – 2300 light years away – is easily visible through binoculars, and even to the unaided eye. It's rumoured that the Greek philosopher Aristotle, in 325 BC, called it 'a cloudy spot' – the earliest description of a deep-sky object.

FEBRUARY'S OBJECT

Known to generations of schoolkids as 'Beetle Juice', **Betelgeuse** is one of the biggest and most luminous stars known. If placed in the Solar System, it would swamp the planets all the way to the asteroid belt – possibly as far as Jupiter. It's over 100,000 times brighter than the Sun.

Almost 1000 times wider than the Sun, Betelgeuse is a red supergiant – a star close to the end of its life. It's one of just a few stars to be imaged as a visible disc from Earth, by specialised telescopes. Betelgeuse has suffered middle-age spread as frenetic nuclear reactions in the star's core have forced its outer layers to swell and cool. The star also fluctuates slightly in brightness as it tries to get a grip on its billowing gases. Early in 2020, Betelgeuse dimmed to its faintest in over a century, appearing no more prominent than the other shoulder-star **Bellatrix**.

OBSERVING TIP

When you first go out to observe, you may be disappointed at how few stars you can see in the sky. But wait for 20 minutes, and you'll be amazed at how your night vision improves. One reason for this 'dark adaption' is that the pupil of your eye grows larger. More importantly, in dark conditions the retina of your eye builds up bigger reserves of rhodopsin, the chemical that responds to light.

Betelgeuse will exit the cosmic scene in a spectacular supernova explosion. As a result of the breakdown of nuclear reactions at its heart, the star will explode – to shine as brightly in our skies as the Full Moon.

FEBRUARY'S TOPIC: LIFE ON MARS

Is there life on **Mars**? This could be the year we find out. This month, a flotilla of ambitious probes, launched from Earth in 2020, arrives at the Red Planet (see Special Events), to comb and analyse its surface in detail.

It took British astronomer Sara Wager, observing from Olocau in Spain, a total of 48 hours to acquire the data for this beautiful image. Her telescope was a 250-mm Orion Optics ODK10, equipped with a QSI 683 camera, and she took 89 exposures through different coloured filters.

These are the first biological probes since NASA's Vikings in 1976. Each Viking lander contained four experiments – one of which gave a positive result. Designed by sanitary engineer Gil Levin, the Labelled Release experiment was simplicity: put some Martian soil in water, and feed it some nutrient. If there were bugs present, they would give off gas. (The gas was spiced with a radioactive marker to make the experiment more sensitive.) As the bugs reproduced, the gas would build up. And that's exactly what happened. But Levin's colleagues were sceptical, and put the findings down to 'chemistry'. They came back to NASA with a negative result.

So, for the last 40 years, NASA has only explored the geology of Mars with its army of robots and rovers. But out of the geology there have come a lot of biological clues, especially indicators for life, such as water. There's evidence for former lakes; even a great ocean. Scientists think this may have gone to ground as permafrost. And some recent gullies may have been cut by running water.

Most exciting has been the discovery of reactive methane gas in the Red Planet's atmosphere. Does it come from volcanoes? Or from primitive bacteria...?

Now it's the biologists' turn to take over the Red Planet. Happy landings!

FEBRUARY'S PICTURE

The **Pinwheel Galaxy** (officially called M101) lies 21 million light years away in **Ursa Major**. This stunning spiral galaxy measures 170,000 light years across, rather larger than the Milky Way. It boasts a trillion stars – twice as many as our Galaxy – which are beautifully displayed in this face-on image taken by Sara Wager. Many of its stars have yet to form: huge glowing nebulae in the galaxy's spiral arms mark the spots where starbirth is taking place today.

SUNDAY	MONDAY	TUESDAY	WEDNESDAY	THURSDAY	FRIDAY	SATURDAY
	1	2 Moon near Spica	3	4 5.37 pm Last Quarter Moon	5	6 Moon near Antares (am)
7	8	9	10	11 7.05 pm New Moon	12	13
14	15	16	17	18 Moon near Mars and the Pleiades	19 6.47 pm First Quarter Moon between the Pleiades and the Hyades/Aldebaran	20
21	22	23 Moon near Castor and Pollux	24 Moon near Praesepe	25	26 Moon near Regulus	27 8.17 am Full Moon
28						

Mars

SPECIAL EVENTS

- **18 February:** the reddish 'star' above the Moon is the planet Mars; above them lie the Pleiades.
- **19 February:** to the left of the First Quarter Moon you'll find Aldebaran and the Hyades star cluster, while to its right lie the Pleiades and the Red Planet Mars (see Planet Watch and Chart 2a).
- This month, or soon after, three ambitious space missions should reach Mars. NASA's Perseverance rover will find and cache rocks that may bear traces of life, to be returned to Earth by a future mission. It also carries a miniature helicopter for aerial surveys.

China is sending both an orbiter and a small rover, while the United Arab Emirates's Hope mission will survey the atmosphere from orbit. The Exomars mission, originally planned to land this month, has been delayed for two years; it has a Russian fixed base and a European rover intended to search for life on the planet.

2b 27 February, 6.30 am. Jupiter, Mercury and Saturn.

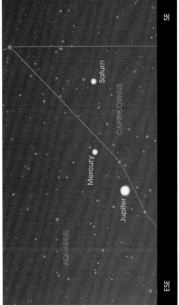

2a 19 February, 10 pm. The Moon and Mars near the Pleiades, the Hyades and Aldebaran.

- The Red Planet pretty much has February's dark hours to itself, brightening up the south-western sky until it sets around 1.15 am. Mars starts the month at magnitude +0.4, but fades to magnitude +0.9 as it moves from Aries to Taurus. There's a lovely sight on 18 and 19 February, when the crescent Moon joins Mars near the Pleiades (the Seven Sisters) star cluster (Chart 2a).

- The two outermost planets lie to the lower right of Mars: Neptune (magnitude +7.9), in Aquarius, sets about 7.30 pm, while slightly brighter Uranus at magnitude +5.8 lies in Aries and sinks below the horizon around midnight.

- On the first couple of nights of February, you may catch Mercury very low in the south-west, at magnitude +1.4 and setting about 6 pm. It then swings between us and the Sun, to reappear in the morning sky in the last week of the month.

- Here, Mercury (now magnitude +0.5) joins the Solar System's two giants, which emerge from the Sun's glare at the end of February. To the left is brilliant Jupiter, at magnitude –2.0. Mercury lies in the middle, and Saturn (magnitude +0.7) to the right (Chart 2b). The trio of planets rises around 6 am.

- Venus lies too close to the Sun to be easily seen this month.

The Pleiades

FEBRUARY'S PLANET WATCH

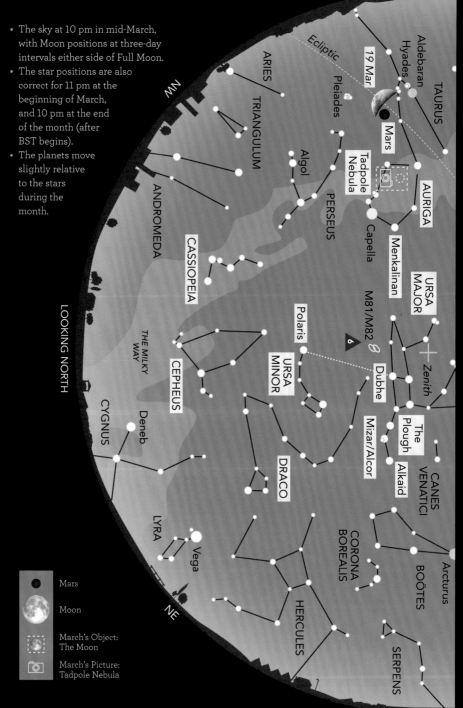

- The sky at 10 pm in mid-March, with Moon positions at three-day intervals either side of Full Moon.
- The star positions are also correct for 11 pm at the beginning of March, and 10 pm at the end of the month (after BST begins).
- The planets move slightly relative to the stars during the month.

LOOKING NORTH

WEST

NW

NE

EAST

Mars

Moon

March's Object: The Moon

March's Picture: Tadpole Nebula

TAURUS
Aldebaran
Hyades
Ecliptic
19 Mar
Mars
ARIES
Pleiades
TRIANGULUM
Algol
Tadpole Nebula
AURIGA
Menkalinan
PERSEUS
Capella
URSA MAJOR
ANDROMEDA
CASSIOPEIA
M81/M82
Polaris
Zenith
THE MILKY WAY
CEPHEUS
URSA MINOR
Dubhe
The Plough
CYGNUS
Deneb
DRACO
Mizar/Alcor
Alkaid
CANES VENATICI
LYRA
Vega
CORONA BOREALIS
BOÖTES
Arcturus
HERCULES
SERPENS

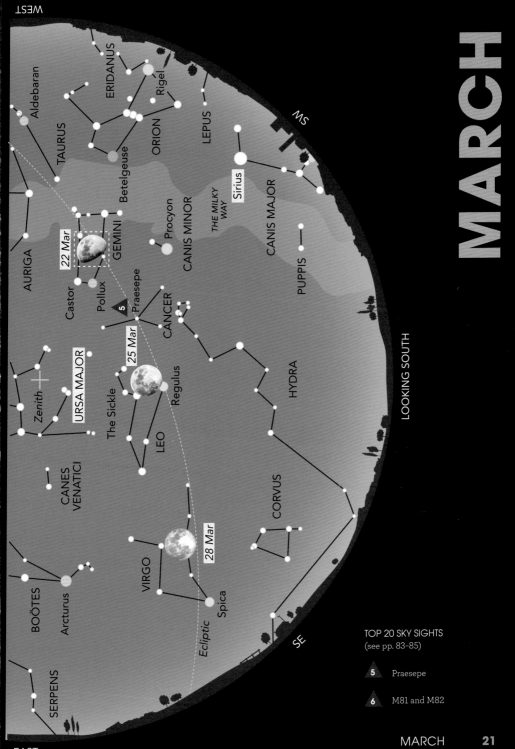

MARCH

Aldebaran

ERIDANUS

Rigel

TAURUS

ORION

Betelgeuse

LEPUS

SW

Sirius

22 Mar

GEMINI

Procyon

CANIS MINOR

THE MILKY WAY

CANIS MAJOR

AURIGA

Castor

Pollux

Praesepe

5

CANCER

PUPPIS

25 Mar

The Sickle

Regulus

URSA MAJOR

Zenith

LEO

HYDRA

LOOKING SOUTH

CANES VENATICI

28 Mar

VIRGO

CORVUS

BOÖTES

Arcturus

Spica

Ecliptic

SE

SERPENS

TOP 20 SKY SIGHTS
(see pp. 83–85)

5 Praesepe

6 M81 and M82

MARCH

Spring is here! On 20 March, we celebrate the Equinox, when day becomes longer than the night, while British Summer Time starts on 28 March. Though our attention each month usually focuses on the changing action in the southern part of the sky, we shouldn't forget the northern constellations that are visible every night of the year: Queen **Cassiopeia** and her consort **Cepheus**, **Draco** (the Dragon), and the two Bears – **Ursa Major** and **Ursa Minor**.

MARCH'S CONSTELLATION

Ursa Major, the Great Bear, is an internationally favourite constellation. In Britain, its seven brightest stars are called **the Plough**. Children today generally haven't seen an old-fashioned horse-drawn plough, and we've found them naming this star pattern 'the saucepan'. In North America, it's known as the Big Dipper.

The Plough is the first star pattern that most people get to know. It's always on view in the northern hemisphere, and the two end stars of the 'bowl' of the Plough point directly towards the Pole Star, **Polaris**, which always lies due north.

Ursa Major is unusual in a couple of ways. First, it contains a double star that you can split with the naked eye: **Mizar**, the star in the middle of the bear's tail (or the handle of the saucepan) has a fainter companion, **Alcor** (see January's Object).

And – unlike most constellations – the majority of the stars in the Plough lie at the same distance and were born together. Leaving aside **Dubhe** and **Alkaid**, the others are all moving in the same direction, along with other stars of the Ursa Major Moving Group, which include brilliant **Sirius** and **Menkalinan** in **Auriga**. Over thousands of years, the shape of the Plough will gradually change, as Dubhe and Alkaid go off on their own paths.

MARCH'S OBJECT

The Moon is our nearest celestial companion, lying a mere 384,400 kilometres away. At 3,476 kilometres across, it's so large compared to Earth that – from space – the system looks like a double planet.

But the Moon couldn't be more different from our verdant Earth. Bereft of an atmosphere, it's constantly exposed to bombardment by meteorites and asteroids. Even with the unaided eye, you can see the evidence. The 'face' of the 'Man in the Moon' consists of huge craters created by asteroid hits 3.8 billion years ago.

Through binoculars or a telescope, the surface of the Moon looks amazing – as if you're flying over it. But don't observe our satellite when it's Full: the

OBSERVING TIP

This is the ideal time of year to tie down the main compass directions, as seen from your observing site. North is easy – just latch onto Polaris, the Pole Star, using the familiar stars of the Plough (see Constellation and Star Chart). And at noon, the Sun is always in the south. But the useful extra in March is that we hit the Spring Equinox, when the Sun rises due east, and sets due west. So remember those positions relative to a tree or house around your horizon.

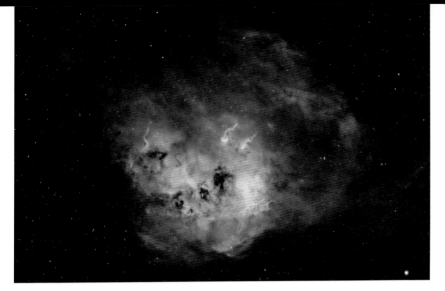

Peter Jenkins captured this image from his home in Kirkby-in-Ashfield, Nottinghamshire, using an Officina Stellare Hiper Apo 115-mm refractor with an Atik Horizon Mono camera. It comprises 20 × 5-minute exposures each through hydrogen, oxygen and sulphur filters, together with 1 × 30-second exposure through red, green and blue filters to provide natural star colours. The total exposure time was almost 5.5 hours.

light is flat, and swamps its features. It's best to roam the Moon when it's a crescent or half-lit, and see the sideways-on shadows highlighting its dramatic relief.

MARCH'S TOPIC: ZODIACAL LIGHT

At this time of year, the Zodiac rises steeply from the horizon at dusk. That word may evoke all the mumbo-jumbo of astrology, but in astronomy the Zodiac is simply the track that the planets pursue around the sky. And now is the time to observe one of its most elusive phenomena: the zodiacal light.

On a really clear night, away from streetlights, you may spot a faint pyramid of light in the west just after the Sun has gone down. This ghostly glow is the zodiacal light.

It's also visible in the morning sky. The 12th-century poet and astronomer Omar Khayyam had a fantastic view of a 'false dawn' over the Persian desert. In typical fashion, he celebrated with wine – and wrote a poem: 'When false dawn streaks the east with cold, grey line, pour in your cups the pure blood of the vine'.

It's so rarely seen that many astronomers have never witnessed it. But persevere! It's caused by light reflected from a fog of tiny particles filling the inner Solar System, the remains of old comets and asteroids that have broken up. As our planet orbits the Sun, the Earth scoops up around 40,000 tonnes of this space dust every year.

MARCH'S PICTURE

Some 12,000 light years away in **Auriga**, the **Tadpole Nebula** is a star nursery that was born 4 million years ago. Here, Peter Jenkins has scooped up the features that give this nebula its name: two tadpole-shaped dust clouds, to the upper right of the bright region. Although they may look like tiddlers, each cosmic tadpole is around ten light years long. They swim in a nebula that's 100 light years across.

SUNDAY	MONDAY	TUESDAY	WEDNESDAY	THURSDAY	FRIDAY	SATURDAY
	1 Moon near Spica	2 Moon near Spica	3 Mars near the Pleiades	4	5 Moon near Antares (am); Mercury close to Jupiter (am)	6 1.30 am Last Quarter Moon near Antares (am); Mercury W elongation
7	8	9	10 Crescent Moon near Mercury, Jupiter and Saturn (am)	11	12	13 10.21 am New Moon
14	15	16	17	18 Moon near the Pleiades	19 Moon between Aldebaran and Mars, near the Hyades and the Pleiades	20 Spring Equinox
21 2.40 pm First Quarter Moon	22	23 Moon near Castor and Pollux	24	25 Moon near Regulus	26	27
28 BST begins; 7.48 pm Full Moon, supermoon	29 Moon near Spica	30	31			

SPECIAL EVENTS

- **3 March:** Mars passes below the Pleiades (see Planet Watch).
- **5 March, 6.15 am:** Mercury only 17 arcminutes above Jupiter (see Planet Watch and Chart 3a).
- **10 March, 6 am:** scan very low on the south-east horizon to see a narrow crescent Moon below Mercury, Jupiter and Saturn (binoculars will help).
- **18 March:** above the crescent Moon you'll find the Pleiades (upper right), with Aldebaran, the Hyades and Mars to the upper left.
- **19 March:** the Moon lies very close to Mars (upper right), with the Pleiades well to the right, and Aldebaran with the Hyades to the lower left of the Moon (see Planet Watch and Chart 3b).
- **20 March, 9.37 am:** the Spring Equinox, when day and night are equal.
- **28 March, 1.00 am:** British Summer Time starts – don't forget to put your clocks forward.
- **28 March:** the first of four **supermoons** this year, when the Full Moon is unusually near and bright. (The best supermoon will be on 26 May.)

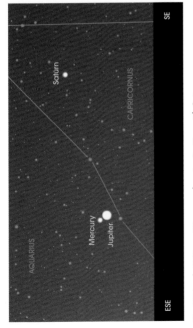

3a *5 March, 6.15 am. Mercury close to Jupiter, with Saturn.*

3b *19 March, 10 pm. The Moon close to Mars, between the Pleiades and the Hyades/Aldebaran.*

• In the western sky, we have two red 'stars'. To the left is red giant Aldebaran, marking the eye of Taurus, while to the right lies **Mars.** The Red Planet (setting around 1 am) starts the month at magnitude +0.9, very similar to Aldebaran, but fades to +1.3 by the end of March. Travelling through Taurus, Mars makes a delicious tableau with the Pleiades during the first week of the month. It's nearest to Aldebaran on 19 March, when the Moon joins them (Chart 3b).

• **Uranus,** in Aries, is borderline naked-eye brightness at magnitude +5.8, and sets about 10 pm.

• Over to the morning sky for the rest of the planetary action... In the south-east, the largest world, **Jupiter,** shines at a brilliant magnitude –2.0. To the right lies its smaller sibling, **Saturn,** at magnitude +0.7. Both planets are inhabiting Capricornus, and rise at around 5 am.

• At the start of March, **Mercury** lies just to the upper right of Jupiter at magnitude +0.2. Moving leftwards, the innermost planet passes just 17 arcminutes above Jupiter on the morning of 5 March (Chart 3a). On 6 March, Mercury is at its maximum separation from the Sun; it then sinks into the dawn twilight and disappears mid-month.

• **Venus** and **Neptune** are lost in the Sun's glare in March.

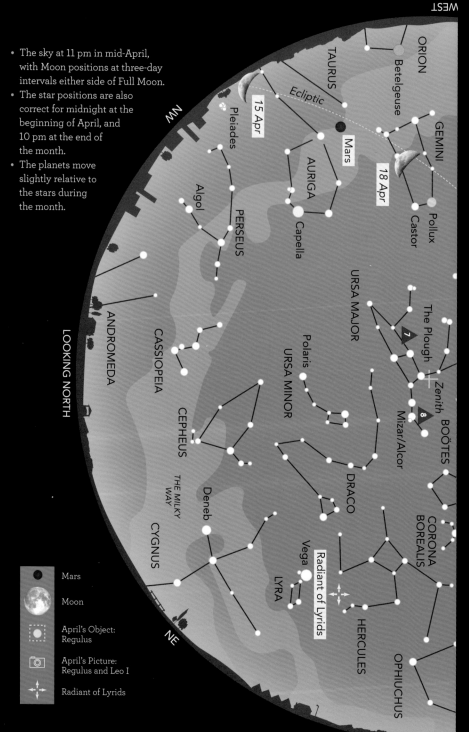

- The sky at 11 pm in mid-April, with Moon positions at three-day intervals either side of Full Moon.
- The star positions are also correct for midnight at the beginning of April, and 10 pm at the end of the month.
- The planets move slightly relative to the stars during the month.

WEST

ORION
Betelgeuse
TAURUS
Ecliptic
15 Apr
Pleiades
Mars
18 Apr
GEMINI
Pollux
Castor
Algol
AURIGA
Capella
PERSEUS
URSA MAJOR
The Plough
7
Zenith
Mizar/Alcor
8
BOÖTES
NW
Polaris
URSA MINOR
CORONA
BOREALIS
ANDROMEDA
LOOKING NORTH
CASSIOPEIA
CEPHEUS
DRACO
THE MILKY WAY
Deneb
Vega
Radiant of Lyrids
HERCULES
CYGNUS
LYRA
OPHIUCHUS
NE

Mars

Moon

April's Object: Regulus

April's Picture: Regulus and Leo I

Radiant of Lyrids

EAST

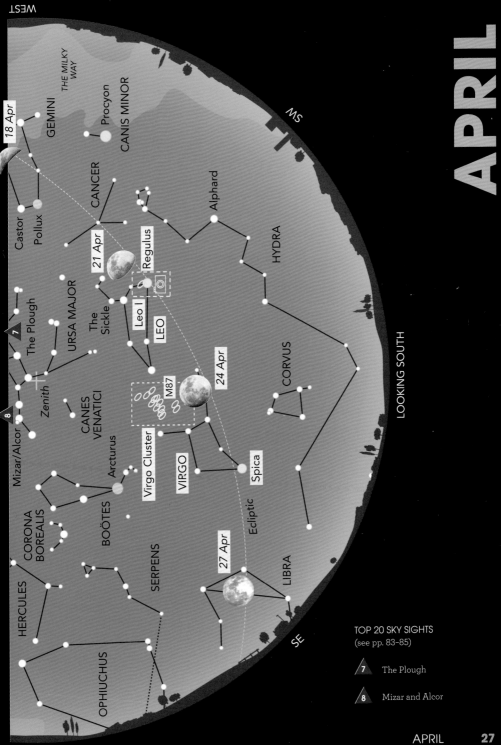

WEST

APRIL

THE MILKY WAY

GEMINI

Procyon

CANIS MINOR

18 Apr

Castor
Pollux

CANCER

SW

21 Apr

Regulus

Alphard

HYDRA

URSA MAJOR

The Plough

7

The Sickle

Leo I

LEO

CANES
VENATICI

Zenith

24 Apr

M87

CORVUS

LOOKING SOUTH

Mizar/Alcor

8

Virgo Cluster

Arcturus

VIRGO

Spica

CORONA
BOREALIS

BOÖTES

27 Apr

Ecliptic

HERCULES

SERPENS

LIBRA

SE

OPHIUCHUS

TOP 20 SKY SIGHTS
(see pp. 83–85)

7 The Plough

8 Mizar and Alcor

EAST

APRIL 27

APRIL

The ancient constellations of **Leo** (the Lion) and **Virgo** (the Virgin) dominate the springtime skies. Leo does indeed look like a recumbent lion, but it's hard to envisage Virgo as anything other than a vast 'Y' in the sky! And the dusk twilight is brightened up at the end of the month by both the Sun-hugging planets: Venus and Mercury.

APRIL'S CONSTELLATION

The Y-shaped constellation of **Virgo** is the second largest in the sky. It may take a bit of imagination to see this group of stars as a virtuous maiden holding an ear of corn (the bright star **Spica**), but this ancient constellation is associated with the time of harvest because the Sun passes through Virgo in the early months of autumn.

Spica is a hot, blue-white star over 20,000 times brighter than the Sun, boasting a temperature of 25,000 °C. It has a stellar companion, which lies just 18 million kilometres away from Spica – closer than Mercury orbits the Sun. Both stars inflict a mighty gravitational toll on each other, raising enormous tides and creating two distorted, egg-shaped stars.

The glory of Virgo lies in the 'bowl' of the Y-shape. Scan the upper region with

OBSERVING TIP

Don't think that you need a telescope to bring the heavens closer. Binoculars are excellent – and you can fling them into the back of the car at the last minute. For astronomy, buy binoculars with large lenses coupled with a modest magnification. An ideal size is 7 x 50, meaning that the magnification is seven times, and that the diameter of the lenses is 50 millimetres. See Robin Scagell's Choosing & Using Binoculars for more details (pp. 86–89).

a small telescope – at a low magnification – and you'll find it packed with faint, fuzzy blobs. These are just a few of the 2000 galaxies – star cities like the Milky Way – that make up the gigantic **Virgo Cluster**. It's centred on the mammoth galaxy **M87**, which boasts a central black hole over 6 billion times heavier than the Sun: it was the first black hole ever to be imaged, in 2019.

APRIL'S OBJECT

Regulus – the 'heart' of **Leo** – appears to be a bright but run-of-the-mill star. Some 79 light years away, it's young (about a billion years old), 3.8 times heavier than the Sun, and it chucks out 300 times as much energy as our local star. But recent discoveries have revealed it to be a maverick. First, it has at least four companion stars. And Regulus spins in just 16 hours (as compared to roughly a month for our Sun) – meaning that its equator is rotating at over a million kilometres per hour. This crazy spin rate makes the star's equatorial regions bulge out like a tangerine. If it were to spin only 5 per cent faster, Regulus would tear itself apart!

APRIL'S TOPIC: DATE OF EASTER

The moveable feast of eggs and chocolate falls on 4 April this year, in the middle of a range of possible dates that spans 22 March to 25 April. If you've ever wondered why the date of Easter

28   APRIL

changes so much, year by year, it's all to do with astronomy. . . According to the Bible, Jesus was crucified at the Passover, whose date was fixed by the Jewish lunar calendar, based on the Moon's phases. So you can tell when Easter is due just by looking at the sky! First, wait until you see the Sun rising due east and setting due west: that's the Spring Solstice. Now follow the Moon until it's Full – and Easter will be the next Sunday. This year, the Full Moon after the Solstice fell on 28 March, and the following Sunday is 4 April.

APRIL'S PICTURE

The celestial sapphire here is Regulus, the star marking the heart of Leo (see Object). But in this carefully timed exposure, John Bell has also caught a fuzzy object that's 10,000 times fainter. The reddish cloud is the **Leo I** dwarf galaxy; although it shines at magnitude +11, it's difficult to spot through an eyepiece as your eye is dazzled by Regulus. Lying 10,000 times further away than Regulus, at 820,000 light years, Leo I is the most distant of the little galaxies that orbit the Milky Way. Containing only 20 million stars, and ball shaped, it's classified as a dwarf spheroidal galaxy.

From Haversham, near Milton Keynes, John Bell acquired this image with a 250-mm f/4 Newtonian reflector. He took 20 × 1-minute exposures at ISO 8000, with a Sony A7S astro-modified camera.

SUNDAY	MONDAY	TUESDAY	WEDNESDAY	THURSDAY	FRIDAY	SATURDAY
				1	2 Moon near Antares (am)	3
4 11.02 am Last Quarter Moon	5	6 Moon near Saturn and Jupiter (am)	7 Moon near Saturn and Jupiter (am)	8	9	10
11	12 3.31 am New Moon	13	14 Crescent Moon near the Pleiades	15 Crescent Moon between the Pleiades and the Hyades/Aldebaran	16 Moon between Aldebaran and Mars	17 Moon near Mars
18	19 Moon near Castor and Pollux	20 7.59 am First Quarter Moon, near Praesepe	21 Lyrids	22 Lyrids (am); Moon near Regulus	23	24
25 Moon near Spica; Mercury near Venus	26	27 4.31 am Full Moon, supermoon	28	29 Moon near Antares (am)	30	

SPECIAL EVENTS

- **6 April, 6 am:** Saturn lies above the crescent Moon in the morning sky, with Jupiter to the left (Chart 4a).
- **7 April, 6 am:** the brilliant 'star' near the crescent Moon is giant planet Jupiter; Saturn lies to the right (Chart 4a).
- **14 April:** a slender crescent Moon can be seen hanging below the Pleiades.
- **15 April:** Aldebaran and the Hyades lie to the left of the Moon, with the Pleiades to its right.
- **16 April:** the star below the Moon is Aldebaran, while the fainter reddish 'star' above is Mars.
- **17 April:** Mars lies right next to the Moon.

- **Night of 21/22 April:** maximum of the **Lyrid meteor shower**, shooting stars that appear to emanate from the constellation Lyra as debris from **Comet Thatcher** burns up in the Earth's atmosphere. But don't expect too much: moonlight will wash out all but the brightest meteors.

- **25 April:** Mercury passes just to the right of Venus (see Planet Watch).
- **27 April:** the second closest and brightest Full Moon of the year, only slightly inferior to next month's supermoon (26 May).

4a 6–7 April, 6 am. The crescent Moon with Saturn and Jupiter.

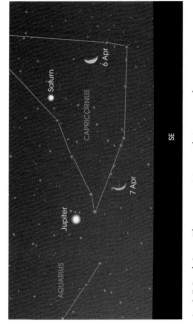

4b 30 April, 9 pm. Venus and Mercury, with the Pleiades, Aldebaran and the Hyades.

Mercury

• **Mars** hangs on in the evening sky, moving from Taurus into Gemini. At magnitude +1.4, the Red Planet sets around 1.30 am.

• Fainter **Uranus** (magnitude +5.9) lies in Aries, and sinks below the horizon about 9 pm.

• In the latter half of the month, **Venus** roars into view after sunset, low in the west. The Evening Star shines at magnitude –3.9, and sets at 9.15 pm by the end of April.

• Travelling along with Venus is its planetary neighbour, **Mercury**. The innermost planet lies just to the right of Venus on 25 April, and ten times fainter, at magnitude –1.6. Over the next week, Mercury rises above the Evening Star and fades slightly to magnitude –1.1 by 30 April (Chart 4b).

• In the morning sky, **Jupiter** and **Saturn** both lie in Capricornus, rising around 4.30 am in the south-east. Giant Jupiter shines at magnitude –2.1, with Saturn rather fainter (magnitude +0.7). The Moon passes near them before dawn on 6 and 7 April (Chart 4a).

• Dim **Neptune** appears from the morning twilight by the end of the month, well to the left of the giants. At magnitude +7.9 and rising around 4.30 am, the most distant planet is to be found in Aquarius.

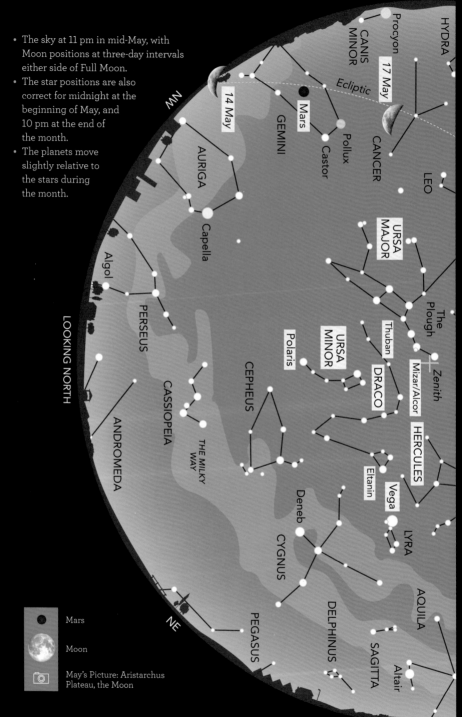

- The sky at 11 pm in mid-May, with Moon positions at three-day intervals either side of Full Moon.
- The star positions are also correct for midnight at the beginning of May, and 10 pm at the end of the month.
- The planets move slightly relative to the stars during the month.

WEST

HYDRA

Procyon

CANIS MINOR

17 May

Ecliptic

Mars

GEMINI

14 May

CANCER

Pollux

Castor

LEO

AURIGA

URSA MAJOR

Capella

The Plough

Algol

Thuban

Zenith

Mizar/Alcor

PERSEUS

URSA MINOR

DRACO

Polaris

HERCULES

LOOKING NORTH

CASSIOPEIA

CEPHEUS

Eltanin

Vega

ANDROMEDA

THE MILKY WAY

Deneb

LYRA

CYGNUS

AQUILA

NE

DELPHINUS

SAGITTA

PEGASUS

Altair

Mars

Moon

May's Picture: Aristarchus Plateau, the Moon

EAST

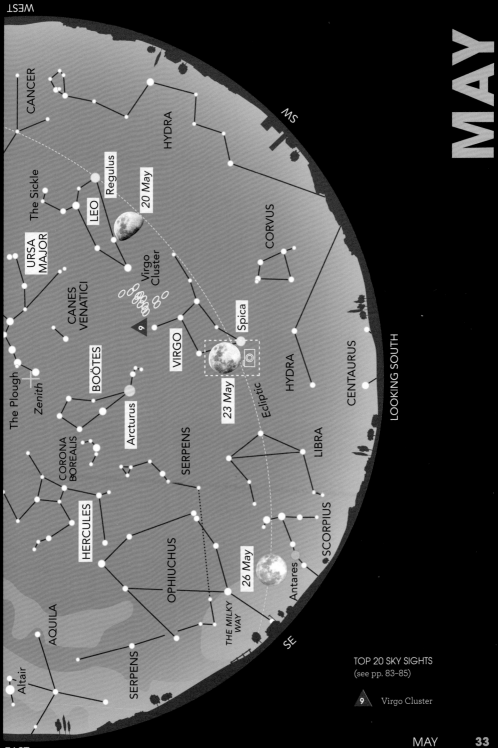

WEST

CANCER

HYDRA

SW

The Sickle

Regulus

LEO

20 May

URSA MAJOR

CANES VENATICI

Virgo Cluster

CORVUS

9

VIRGO

Spica

LOOKING SOUTH

BOÖTES

The Plough

Zenith

Arcturus

CORONA BOREALIS

SERPENS

23 May

HYDRA

Ecliptic

CENTAURUS

HERCULES

SERPENS

LIBRA

OPHIUCHUS

26 May

SCORPIUS

THE MILKY WAY

Antares

AQUILA

SERPENS

SE

Altair

TOP 20 SKY SIGHTS
(see pp. 83–85)

9   Virgo Cluster

EAST

MAY   **33**

We have not just one, but two Evening Stars this month, as brilliant Venus is joined by its fainter little sibling Mercury. Star-wise, orange-coloured **Arcturus**, the principal star of **Boötes** (the Herdsman), forms a giant triangle with two blue-white stars: **Spica**, in **Virgo**, and Leo's shining light **Regulus.**

MAY'S CONSTELLATION

Draco, the cosmic dragon, writhes between the two bears in the northern sky. Draco is associated with the 12 labours of **Hercules**, the head of the constellation firmly under the superhero's feet. In this case, Hercules had to get past a crowd of nymphs and slay a 100-headed dragon (called Ladon) to steal the immortal golden apples guarded by the beast.

The brightest star, **Eltanin**, lies in the dragon's head. This orange star shines at magnitude +2.2, and is 154 light years away. But all this is set to change. In 1.5 million years, it will dash past the Earth at a distance of only 28 light years, blazing as the brightest star in our skies.

Thuban, 300 light years away, lies in the tail of the dragon and stumbles in at a mere magnitude +3.7. But what Thuban lacks in brightness, it makes up for in fame. Thuban was our Pole Star around 2800 BC. It actually lay closer to the celestial pole than **Polaris** does now. That's because the Earth's axis swings around – like the toppling of a spinning top – over a period of 26,000 years. The result of this 'precession' is that the Earth's North Pole points to different stars over the millennia. Look forward to AD 13,600, when brilliant **Vega** will take over the pole. And it will be Thuban's turn again in AD 22,600.

MAY'S OBJECT

This month is your best chance to spot tiny Mercury in the evening sky (see Planet Watch).

This tiny world – just a little bigger than our Moon – is covered in craters. But that's where the resemblance ends. NASA's Messenger spaceprobe discovered that Mercury has a huge core made of molten iron. As the core cooled, the planet shrank, wrinkling its surface like the skin of a dried-up apple. But why should a small world have such a large core? It could be that, during its origins, a collision with another planet blasted off most of its outer rocky layers.

And Messenger's mission highlighted other anomalies. Mercury has a magnetic field: unexpected on a world so small. And, most controversially, Messenger detected traces of water vapour at Mercury's poles. Although the planet

---

OBSERVING TIP

It's always fun to search out the 'faint fuzzies' in the sky – galaxies, star clusters and nebulae. But don't even think of observing dark-sky objects around the time of Full Moon (especially the supermoon this month), as its light will drown them out. You'll have the best views near New Moon: a period astronomers call 'dark of Moon'. When the Moon is bright, though, there's still plenty to see: focus on planets, bright double stars – and, of course, the Moon itself. Check our month-by-month Calendars for the Moon's phases.

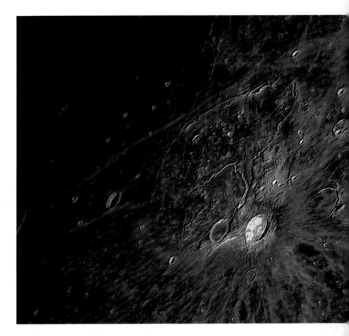

James Harrop imaged the Aristarchus Plateau on 29 January 2018 from Bradford, West Yorkshire, with a 180-mm Sky-Watcher Maksutov telescope and ZWO ASI 224MC camera. He took 5000 frames each with an exposure of 0.016 seconds, using AutoStakkert! software to stack the best images and remove distortions, finally enhancing the colours in Photoshop.

has temperatures that reach 700°C, the cold crater floors at the planet's poles never see sunlight.

About to tackle these questions is the European spaceprobe BepiColombo, launched in October 2018. Researchers must wait until late 2025 before the probe will undoubtedly reveal more about the fleet-footed 'messenger of the gods'.

MAY'S TOPIC: SUPERMOON

We're treated to a particularly big and bright Full Moon on the night of 26 May. Our companion world is at its closest point in 2021 – just 357,314 kilometres away – and appears 14 per cent bigger than when the Moon is at its far point. The Moon is also Full that day, so the brilliant orb will be some 30 per cent more luminous than the faintest Full Moon.

A Full Moon at the closest point in its orbit (perigee) is called a supermoon. This catchy phrase wasn't invented by astronomers, but by astrologers who've tried to link supermoons with earthquakes, tsunamis or volcanic eruptions. But the supermoon's extra gravitational pull is actually only 3 per cent more powerful than average – so we can confidently predict it will cause no natural calamities!

MAY'S PICTURE

Welcome to one of the strangest places on the Moon! Here, James Harrop has homed in on the raised plateau (brown in the image) around the bright crater Aristarchus. This crater is a mere 475 million years old and it hasn't yet been tarnished by exposure to space.

Immediately to its left is the older crater Herodotus, 35 kilometres across. Heading upwards is Schröter's Valley, named after the 18th-century German astronomer Johann Hieronymus Schröter. But this valley wasn't sculpted by running water; it was gouged out by a fiery stream of lava erupting from deep inside the Moon.

SUNDAY	MONDAY	TUESDAY	WEDNESDAY	THURSDAY	FRIDAY	SATURDAY
30	31 Moon near Saturn (am)					1
2	3 Moon near Saturn (am); Mercury near the Pleiades; 8.50 pm Last Quarter Moon	4 Moon between Jupiter and Saturn (am); Mercury near the Pleiades	5 Moon near Jupiter (am)	6 Eta Aquarids (am)	7	8
9 Venus near the Pleiades	10	11 7.59 pm New Moon	12	13 Crescent Moon near Venus and Mercury	14 Moon between Mars and Mercury	15 Moon near Mars
16 Moon near Castor and Pollux	17 Mercury E elongation; Moon near Praesepe	18	19 8.12 pm First Quarter Moon near Regulus	20	21	22
23 Moon near Spica	24	25	26 12.14 pm Full Moon near Antares, supermoon; lunar eclipse	27	28 Mercury near Venus	29

SPECIAL EVENTS

• **3 May:** Mercury and the Pleiades lie above Venus (see Planet Watch).

• **4 May, 5 am:** you'll find Jupiter to the left of the Moon, with Saturn to its upper right.

• **4 May:** Mercury lies just to the left of the Pleiades, with Venus below (see Planet Watch and Chart 5a).

• **Night of 5/6 May:** Shooting stars from the **Eta Aquarid meteor shower** – tiny pieces of **Halley's Comet** burning up in Earth's atmosphere – fly across the sky in the early hours of the morning.

• **9 May:** Venus lies to the left of the Pleiades, with Mercury above (see Planet Watch).

• **13 May:** low in the north-west after sunset, the crescent Moon hangs to the upper left of the Evening Star, Venus. Immediately to the right of the Moon you'll find innermost planet Mercury (Chart 5b).

• **14 May:** in the evening twilight, the Moon lies below Mars and above Mercury, with Venus low on the horizon.

• **15 May:** Mars is just to the upper left of the Moon.

• **26 May:** We are treated to the biggest and brightest Full Moon of 2021, with the Moon just 357,314 km away. This **supermoon** is 30% brighter than the faintest Full Moon. A total lunar eclipse is also visible from the Pacific.

• **28 May:** Mercury passes to the left of Venus (see Planet Watch).

• **31 May, 3.30 am:** the Moon passes below Saturn, with Jupiter to the left.

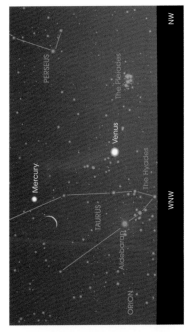

5a *4 May, 8.45 pm. Mercury close to the Pleiades, with Venus, Aldebaran and the Hyades.*

5b *13 May, 9.15 pm. The crescent Moon near Mercury, with Venus, Aldebaran and the Pleiades and Hyades.*

It's an ideal month for spotting the two closest planets to the Sun: you'll find them both in the north-west after sunset. You can't miss **Venus**. Blazing at magnitude –3.9, the Evening Star sets at 9.15 pm at the start of May, and at 10.30 pm by the end of the month.

- **Mercury** lies above Venus almost all month. At the beginning of May, the innermost planet shines at magnitude –1.0 (12 times fainter than Venus). On the evenings of 3 and 4 May, there's a lovely sight as Mercury passes to the left of the Pleiades, with Venus below (Chart 5a). On 9 May, Venus passes the Pleiades, with Mercury above.

- Fading all the time, Mercury rises higher above the Evening Star until 12 May, when it drops back down; the next night the Moon is right next to Mercury (Chart 5b). The planet is at its maximum separation from the Sun on 17 May. By the time Mercury passes just to the left of Venus on 28 May it's over 200 times fainter, at magnitude +2.2.

- **Mars** hangs higher in the evening sky, travelling through Gemini and ending the month near Castor and Pollux. The Red Planet shines at magnitude +1.6 and sets around 0.45 am.

- **Saturn** (magnitude +0.6) rises in the south-east about 2 am, in Capricornus, followed at 2.30 am by **Jupiter**. The giant planet has moved into Aquarius, and shines at magnitude –2.3.

- On the far side of Aquarius, faint **Neptune** (magnitude +7.9) rises around 3 am.

- **Uranus** is lost in the Sun's glare this month.

MAY

MAY'S PLANET WATCH

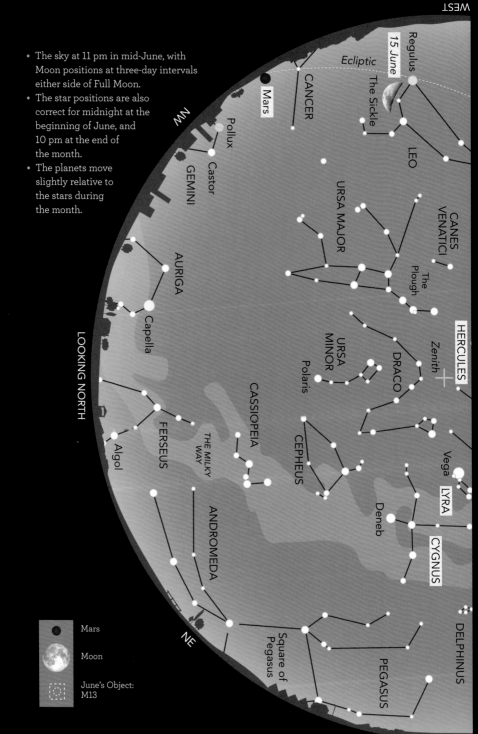

- The sky at 11 pm in mid-June, with Moon positions at three-day intervals either side of Full Moon.
- The star positions are also correct for midnight at the beginning of June, and 10 pm at the end of the month.
- The planets move slightly relative to the stars during the month.

WEST

15 June

Regulus

Ecliptic

The Sickle

Mars

CANCER

LEO

Pollux

CANES VENATICI

Castor

GEMINI

URSA MAJOR

The Plough

NW

AURIGA

HERCULES

Zenith

Capella

URSA MINOR

LOOKING NORTH

Polaris

DRACO

Vega

CASSIOPEIA

LYRA

PERSEUS

THE MILKY WAY

CEPHEUS

Algol

CYGNUS

Deneb

ANDROMEDA

DELPHINUS

NE

Square of Pegasus

PEGASUS

Mars

Moon

June's Object: M13

EAST

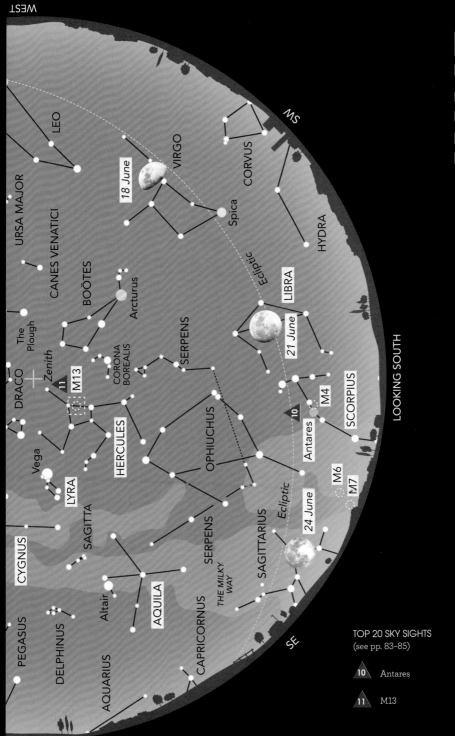

JUNE

URSA MAJOR

LEO

CANES VENATICI

VIRGO

18 June

Spica

CORVUS

HYDRA

SW

BOÖTES

Arcturus

The Plough

Zenith

DRACO

CORONA BOREALIS

SERPENS

LIBRA

21 June

Ecliptic

M13

11

HERCULES

OPHIUCHUS

Antares

10

M4

SCORPIUS

Vega

LYRA

SAGITTA

SERPENS

Ecliptic

M6

M7

CYGNUS

SAGITTARIUS

24 June

PEGASUS

Altair

AQUILA

CAPRICORNUS

THE MILKY WAY

DELPHINUS

AQUARIUS

SE

TOP 20 SKY SIGHTS
(see pp. 83–85)

10 Antares

11 M13

This month, we're treated to an eclipse of the Sun, the first in six years. Don't get too excited: it's not total, but depending on where you are in the country, between 20 and 35 per cent of the Sun's disc is obscured by the Moon on 10 June (see Special Events and Observing Tip). After dark, acquaint yourself with the lovely summer constellations of **Hercules**, **Scorpius**, **Lyra**, **Cygnus** and **Aquila**.

JUNE'S CONSTELLATION

Down in the deep south of the sky lies a baleful red star. **Antares** – 'the rival of Mars' – surpasses in ruddiness even the famed Red Planet. To the ancient Greeks, Antares marked the heart of **Scorpius**, the celestial scorpion. They intimately linked this summer constellation with the winter star pattern Orion, who was killed by a mighty scorpion. The gods placed both in the sky, but at opposite sides, so Orion sets as Scorpius rises.

Unusually, Scorpius resembles its terrestrial namesake. A line of stars to the top right of Antares marks the scorpion's forelimbs. Originally, the stars we now call **Libra** (the Scales) were its claws. Below Antares, the scorpion's body stretches down into a fine curved tail (below the horizon on the chart), and

deadly sting. Alas, these aren't visible from the latitude of the UK: an excuse for a Mediterranean holiday!

Scorpius is a treasure trove of astronomical goodies. Several lovely double stars include Antares: its faint companion looks greenish in contrast to Antares's strong red hue. Binoculars reveal the fuzzy patch of **M4**, a globular cluster made of tens of thousands of stars, some 7200 light years away. Above the sting lie two fine star clusters – **M6** and **M7** – visible to the naked eye when they're well above the horizon: a telescope reveals their stars clearly.

Nigel snapped this picture on 22 November 2019 with his Samsung Galaxy S10e smartphone in automatic mode, propping his elbows on a wall for stability. The phone chose a 0.1-second exposure on f/1.5 with a speed of ISO-640.

JUNE'S OBJECT

At the darkest part of a June night, you may spot a faint fuzzy patch way up high in the south, in the constellation **Hercules**. Through binoculars, it appears as a gently glowing ball of light. With a telescope, you can glimpse its true nature: a cluster of almost a million stars, swarming together in space.

This wonderful object is known as **M13**, because it was the 13th entry in the catalogue of fuzzy objects recorded by the 18th-century French astronomer Charles Messier. We now classify M13 as a 'globular cluster'. These great round balls of stars are among the oldest objects in our Galaxy, dating back to its birth some 13 billion years ago.

In 1974, radio astronomers sent a message towards M13, hoping to inform the inhabitants of any planet there of our existence. There's only one problem: M13 lies so far away that we wouldn't receive a reply until AD 46,000!

JUNE'S TOPIC:
NOCTILUCENT CLOUDS

Look north at twilight, and you may be lucky enough to see what has to be the most ghostly apparition in the night sky – noctilucent clouds. Derived from the Latin for 'night shining', these spooky clouds glow blue-white. Illuminated by the Sun after it's set, they're most commonly seen between latitudes 50° and 70° in the summer, when the Sun doesn't sink low below the horizon even at midnight.

These are the highest clouds in the sky, occurring around 80 kilometres up in the atmosphere. And their origin is controversial. They're certainly composed of ice, coated around tiny particles of dust – but what is the origin of the dust?

Tellingly, the first observation of noctilucent clouds was made in 1885, two years after the great eruption of Krakatoa. So could the particles be volcanic dust? Others believe that the particles could be micrometeorites, entering the atmosphere at high altitudes. Some scientists put them down to the Industrial Revolution, with its resultant increased pollution.

JUNE'S PICTURE

Co-author Nigel Henbest was without a telescope, camera or tripod when he spotted the spectacular conjunction of Venus and Jupiter in November 2019 from a desert restaurant near Dubai – at a time when the British Isles was largely clouded out. Saturn completed the planetary trio (out of the frame of this image). This picture shows what can be achieved with just a smartphone, on automatic settings!

SUNDAY	MONDAY	TUESDAY	WEDNESDAY	THURSDAY	FRIDAY	SATURDAY
		1 Moon near Jupiter (am)	2 8.24 am Last Quarter Moon, near Jupiter (am)	3	4	5
6	7	8	9	10 11.52 am New Moon; annular solar eclipse (partial in the UK)	11 Crescent Moon near Venus	12 Crescent Moon near Venus
13 Crescent Moon near Mars	14	15 Moon near Regulus	16	17	18 4.54 am First Quarter Moon	19 Moon near Spica
20	21 Summer Solstice	22 Moon near Antares; Venus near Castor and Pollux	23 Mars in front of Praesepe	24 7.39 pm Full Moon, supermoon	25	26
27 Moon near Saturn (am)	28 Moon between Jupiter and Saturn (am)	29 Moon near Jupiter (am)	30			

SPECIAL EVENTS

- **10 June:** an annular solar eclipse – where a ring of the Sun's brilliant surface is visible around the Moon's silhouette – is visible from northern Canada, the North Pole and eastern Siberia. Most of Europe, north-east North America and western Asia will experience a partial eclipse. From London, the Sun is 20% obscured at 11.13 am, rising to 32% (at 11.16 am) as viewed from Glasgow.
- **11 June:** soon after sunset, look to the lower right of glorious Venus to spot the narrowest crescent Moon.
- **12 June:** the crescent Moon lies above Venus, with Mars to the upper left.
- **13 June:** the reddish 'star' right next to the Moon is Mars; Venus is down to the lower right (Chart 6a).
- **21 June, 4.32 am:** Summer Solstice. The Sun reaches its most northerly point in the sky, so today is Midsummer's Day, with the longest period of daylight and the shortest night.
- **23 June:** Mars appears right in the midst of the Praesepe star cluster (see Planet Watch and Chart 6b).
- **27 June, 2 am:** to the left of the Moon you'll see Saturn and, further on, giant planet Jupiter.
- **28 June, 2 am:** the Moon lies between Jupiter (left) and Saturn (right).
- **29 June, 2 am:** Jupiter and the Moon are up close and personal.

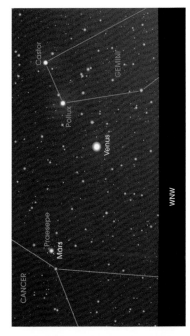

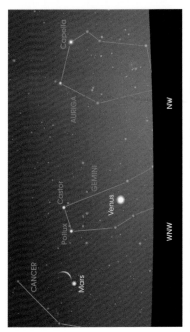

6a 13 June, 10 pm. The Moon close to Mars, with Venus, Pollux, Castor and Capella.

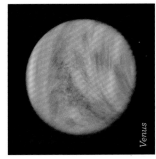

6b 23 June, 10 pm. Mars in Praesepe, with Venus, Pollux and Castor.

- Brilliant **Venus** dominates the evening sky after sunset. At magnitude –3.9, it's brighter than anything in the night sky bar the Moon. Setting around 11 pm, the Evening Star passes to the left of Castor and Pollux on 22 June.

- Venus is heading inexorably towards **Mars**, to its upper left. The Red Planet is almost 200 times fainter, at magnitude +1.8. Starting the month near Castor and Pollux, during June it moves from Gemini into Cancer.

On 23 June, you can see it smack bang in front of the Praesepe star cluster (Chart 6b). Though it's low in the evening twilight, this will be a gorgeous sight in binoculars or a small telescope.

- We have a pair of giant planets over in the south-east before dawn. The fainter, at magnitude +0.5, is **Saturn**, lying in Capricornus and rising around midnight.

To its left, giant **Jupiter** comes above the horizon about 0.30 am in Aquarius, and shines at a glorious magnitude –2.5.

- They are followed by dim **Neptune**, on the borders of Aquarius and Pisces. The most distant planet rises about 1.30 am and sulks at a mere magnitude +7.9.

- **Mercury** and **Uranus** are too close to the Sun to be easily seen this month.

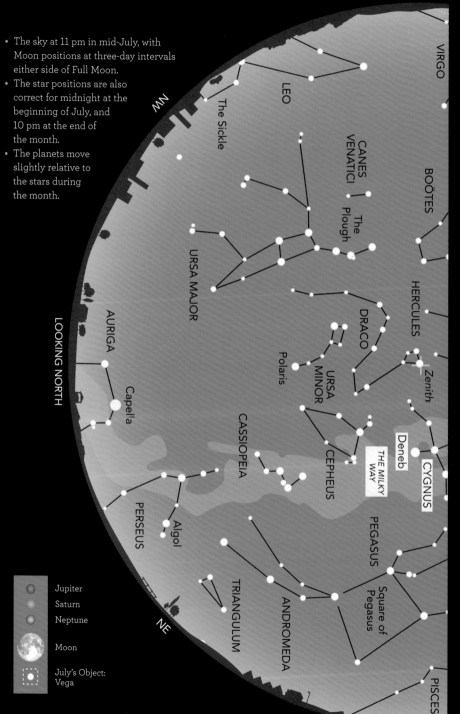

- The sky at 11 pm in mid-July, with Moon positions at three-day intervals either side of Full Moon.
- The star positions are also correct for midnight at the beginning of July, and 10 pm at the end of the month.
- The planets move slightly relative to the stars during the month.

WEST

VIRGO

NW

LEO

The Sickle

CANES VENATICI

BOÖTES

The Plough

URSA MAJOR

HERCULES

LOOKING NORTH

AURIGA

DRACO

Capella

Polaris

URSA MINOR

Zenith

CASSIOPEIA

CEPHEUS

Deneb

THE MILKY WAY

CYGNUS

PERSEUS

Algol

PEGASUS

Square of Pegasus

NE

TRIANGULUM

ANDROMEDA

Jupiter
Saturn
Neptune

Moon

July's Object: Vega

PISCES

EAST

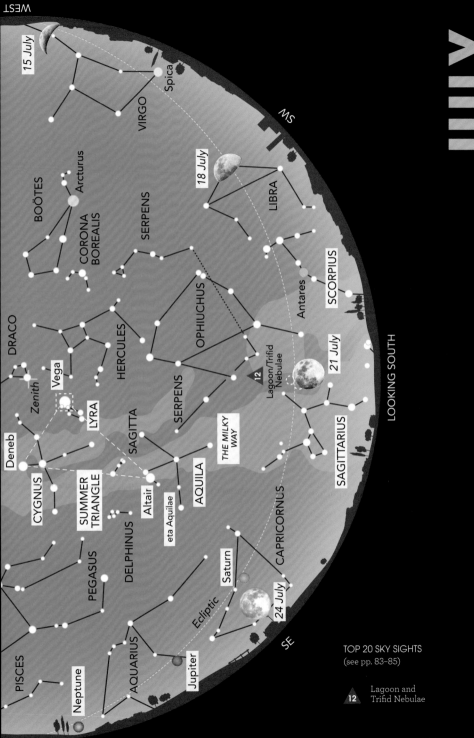

JULY

WEST

15 July

VIRGO

Spica

MS

BOÖTES

Arcturus

CORONA
BOREALIS

SERPENS

18 July

LIBRA

DRACO

HERCULES

SERPENS

OPHIUCHUS

Antares

SCORPIUS

Zenith

Vega

LYRA

SAGITTA

SERPENS

12
Lagoon/Trifid
Nebulae

21 July

LOOKING SOUTH

Deneb

CYGNUS

SUMMER
TRIANGLE

Altair

AQUILA

THE MILKY
WAY

SAGITTARIUS

DELPHINUS

eta Aquilae

PEGASUS

CAPRICORNUS

PISCES

AQUARIUS

Saturn

Ecliptic

24 July

SE

Neptune

Jupiter

TOP 20 SKY SIGHTS
(see pp. 83–85)

12   Lagoon and
Trifid Nebulae

EAST

JULY   **45**

Linger outside on a warm summer evening, and enjoy the treat of four planets on display: Venus, Mars, **Jupiter** and **Saturn**. As the sky grows darker and the stars gradually emerge, pick out the constellations on display in the middle of the year. Low in the south lie **Sagittarius** and **Scorpius**, embedded in the glorious heart of the **Milky Way**. Higher in the sky, the prominent **Summer Triangle** is composed of **Vega**, **Deneb** and **Altair**, the leading lights of **Lyra**, **Cygnus** and **Aquila**.

JULY'S CONSTELLATION

It has to be admitted that **Aquila** does vaguely resemble a flying eagle, albeit a rather faint one. It's an ancient constellation, named after the bird that was a companion to the god Jupiter. The pet eagle carried the mighty god's thunderbolts, and – according to one legend – scooped up the Trojan youth Ganymede when Jupiter took a shine to the beautiful boy.

The constellation is dominated by **Altair**, a young blue-white star 17 light years away, which is 11 times brighter than our Sun. It has a very fast spin, rotating in just nine hours (as opposed to about a month for the Sun), so its equator is hurtling around at 210 kilometres per second. Altair has two fainter companions, making it a triple star.

OBSERVING TIP

This is the month when you really need a good, unobstructed horizon to the south, for the best views of the glorious summer constellations of Scorpius and Sagittarius. They never rise high in temperate latitudes, so make the best of a southerly view – especially over the sea – if you're away on holiday. A good southern horizon is also best for views of the planets, because they rise highest when they're in the south.

Eta Aquilae is one of the brightest Cepheid variable stars – old stars that change their brightness by swelling and shrinking. The pulsations of eta Aquilae make it vary from magnitude +3.4 to +4.4 every seven days.

JULY'S OBJECT

One of our favourite stars – **Vega**, in **Lyra** – lies almost at the zenith for the summer months. Because the Earth's axis gradually wobbles and the north pole changes its direction in space (see May's Constellation), brilliant Vega was our Pole Star around 12,000 BC and will be again in AD 13,600.

The fifth-brightest star in the sky, Vega has the honour to have been the first star photographed, after the Sun. It is pure white: so pure that its colour is used as a benchmark to measure the colours of other stars – from red to blue-white – and so gauge their temperatures.

The star is a whirling dervish. It rotates in just 12.5 hours, and – as a result – its equator bulges outwards, making Vega satsuma-shaped.

Vega was one of the first stars around which astronomers discovered a warm, dusty disc. A ring of dust around a very young star often comprises material forming into new planets, but Vega is a more mature 450 million years old. Here we're probably seeing the debris from a collision between large asteroids. There are strong suspicions that planets may lurk in Vega's dusty disc, too.

JULY'S TOPIC:
CECILIA PAYNE-GAPOSCHKIN

Open any astronomy book today, and you'll learn that most of the Universe is made of hydrogen. That's a relatively rare gas on Earth, so the discovery – in the 1920s – was quite a surprise. And it was made by one of our great unsung heroes of astronomy, Cecilia Payne-Gaposchkin.

Born in the small market town of Wendover in Buckinghamshire in 1900, the sight of a spectacular meteor when she was five inspired her to become an astronomer – like co-author of this book, Heather – even though female scientists were then a rarity.

Her talents led to a place at Harvard University, Massachusetts, to study for a doctorate. By analysing the light from the Sun, split into a spectrum of colours, she was the first to deduce that it's made almost entirely of hydrogen. Later, her work *Stellar Atmospheres* was hailed as 'the most brilliant PhD thesis ever written in astronomy'.

But, at first, her older male colleagues were hard to win over. Only after they had repeated her work a few years later did the penny finally drop.

In 1977, just three years before her death, Payne-Gaposchkin won a prestigious astronomy award and, in her acceptance speech, she told the audience: 'The reward of a young scientist is the emotional thrill of being the first person in the history of the world to see something or to understand something. Nothing can compare with that experience'.

JULY'S PICTURE

Pete Lawrence's stunning close-up of the Sun's surface shows a giant sunspot, the size of planet Earth. It's a complex of magnetic fields, confining the Sun's brilliant roiling gases. This spot was a last gasp in the 11-year cycle of solar activity that's just finished. After solar minimum, new spots are now appearing and astronomers expect these dark rashes on the Sun to peak around 2025.

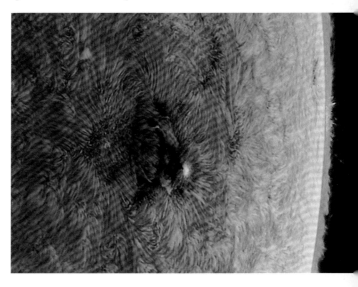

This sunspot, part of active region AR12713, was imaged by Pete Lawrence from Selsey, West Sussex, on 22 June 2018. He took it using a high frame-rate camera (ASI174MM) through a DayStar Quark H-alpha filter fitted to a 102-mm refractor.

SUNDAY	MONDAY	TUESDAY	WEDNESDAY	THURSDAY	FRIDAY	SATURDAY
				1 10.10 pm Last Quarter Moon	**2** Venus near Praesepe	**3** Venus near Praesepe
4 Mercury W elongation	**5** Moon near Pleiades (am); Earth at aphelion	**6** Moon between Pleiades and Aldebaran (am)	**7** Moon near Aldebaran (am)	**8** Moon near Mercury (am)	**9**	**10** 2.16 am New Moon
11 Moon near Venus	**12** Venus near Mars, with Moon nearby	**13** Venus near Mars; Moon near Regulus	**14**	**15**	**16** Moon near Spica	**17** 11.10 am First Quarter Moon near Spica
18	**19**	**20** Moon near Antares	**21** Venus near Regulus	**22**	**23**	**24** 3.37 am Full Moon near Saturn
25 Moon near Jupiter	**26**	**27**	**28**	**29** Mars near Regulus	**30**	**31** 2.16 pm Last Quarter Moon

Crescent Moon

SPECIAL EVENTS

- **2–3 July:** Venus passes Praesepe (see Planet Watch).
- **5 July, 4 am:** the Pleiades are to the left of the crescent Moon.
- **5 July, 11.27 pm:** the Earth is furthest from the Sun (aphelion), at 152 million km.
- **6 July, 4 am:** the slender crescent Moon lies under the Pleiades, with Aldebaran to the lower left.
- **8 July, 4 am:** the thinnest crescent Moon passes just above Mercury, very low on the horizon (binoculars will give the best view).
- **11 July:** you'll find a narrow crescent Moon to the right of brilliant Venus.
- **12 July:** Venus is up close and personal to Mars (see Planet Watch and Chart 7a), with the Moon above and Regulus to the left.
- **13 July:** Venus is near Mars (see Planet Watch), with the Moon and Regulus to the left.
- **24 July:** Saturn is above the Moon, with Jupiter to the left (Chart 7b).
- **25 July:** the Moon passes below Jupiter (Chart 7b).

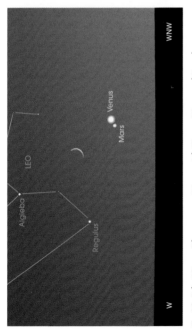

7a 12 July, 10 pm. The crescent Moon with Venus, Mars and Regulus.

7b 23–25 July, 11.30 pm. The Moon passes Saturn and Jupiter.

- In the bright summer twilight, the first thing you'll spot over in the west is the Evening Star. Brilliant **Venus** shines at magnitude –3.9 and sets around 10.30 pm. On 2 and 3 July, the planet grazes the fringes of Praesepe but you'll need binoculars or a telescope to view the event low on the horizon.
- Early in July, Venus is homing in on **Mars**: setting around 10.30 pm, the Red Planet lies in Leo. At magnitude +1.8, Mars is outshone 200 times over by its showy companion. The Planet of Love and the Planet of War hold their tryst on 12 July (Chart 7a).
- Venus then steams off to the left, passing Regulus on 21 July. Mars, following more slowly, lies close to Regulus on 29 July.

- **Saturn** rises about 10 pm, lying in Capricornus at magnitude +0.3. At 10.30 pm it's followed by **Jupiter,** the giant planet shining at magnitude –2.7 in Aquarius.
- After these two giant worlds come the faint outermost planets of the Solar System. **Neptune** (magnitude +7.8) rises at 11.30 pm in Aquarius, while you'll find **Uranus** – in Aries – shining at magnitude +5.8 and rising at 1 am.
- **Mercury** skulks low in the north-east dawn twilight. Though it's at its greatest separation from the Sun on 4 July, you'll see the innermost planet best in the third week of the month, when it rises around 4 am and it brightens to magnitude –1.0.

JULY'S PLANET WATCH

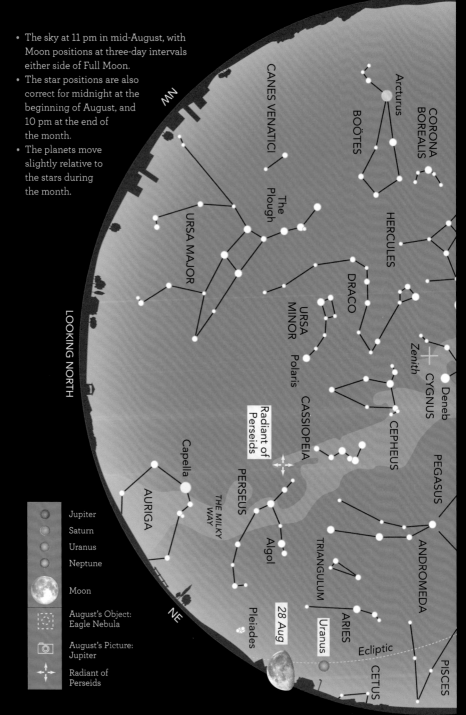

- The sky at 11 pm in mid-August, with Moon positions at three-day intervals either side of Full Moon.
- The star positions are also correct for midnight at the beginning of August, and 10 pm at the end of the month.
- The planets move slightly relative to the stars during the month.

WEST

NW

LOOKING NORTH

NE

EAST

CANES VENATICI

BOÖTES

Arcturus

CORONA BOREALIS

HERCULES

The Plough

URSA MAJOR

DRACO

URSA MINOR

Polaris

Zenith

CYGNUS

Deneb

Radiant of Perseids

CASSIOPEIA

CEPHEUS

PEGASUS

Capella

PERSEUS

THE MILKY WAY

Algol

TRIANGULUM

ANDROMEDA

AURIGA

Pleiades

28 Aug

Uranus

ARIES

Ecliptic

CETUS

PISCES

Jupiter
Saturn
Uranus
Neptune

Moon

August's Object: Eagle Nebula

August's Picture: Jupiter

Radiant of Perseids

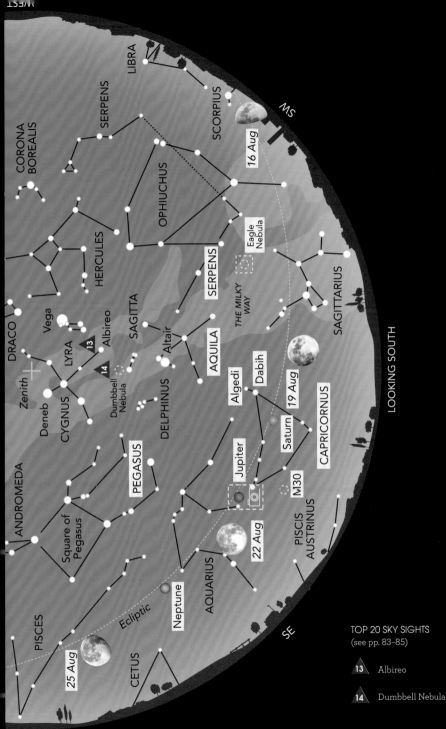

WEST

LIBRA

SERPENS

CORONA BOREALIS

SERPENS

SCORPIUS

16 Aug

MS

OPHIUCHUS

Eagle Nebula

DRACO

HERCULES

SERPENS

SAGITTA

THE MILKY WAY

SAGITTARIUS

Vega

Albireo

13

AQUILA

Altair

LYRA

14

Zenith

Dumbbell Nebula

DELPHINUS

Dabih

Algedi

LOOKING SOUTH

Deneb

CYGNUS

Saturn

19 Aug

ANDROMEDA

PEGASUS

Jupiter

CAPRICORNUS

Square of Pegasus

M30

PISCIS AUSTRINUS

22 Aug

Neptune

AQUARIUS

PISCES

Ecliptic

25 Aug

CETUS

SE

TOP 20 SKY SIGHTS
(see pp. 83–85)

13   Albireo

14   Dumbbell Nebula

EAST

AUGUST   **51**

We have a 'Glorious Twelfth' for astronomers this month: the night of 12 August is the maximum of the **Perseid** meteor shower, one of the most reliable displays of shooting stars. In addition, giant planets **Saturn** and **Jupiter** are at their closest and brightest.

AUGUST'S CONSTELLATION

Capricornus is one of the faint watery constellations that swim in the celestial sea below **Pegasus** – the Winged Horse. But Capricornus had a special significance for ancient peoples. Over 2500 years ago, the Sun nestled among its stars at the time of the Winter Solstice, indicating that the hours of darkness were coming to an end, and life-giving spring was on the way. So this obscure triangle of faint stars may have been one of our first constellations.

Algedi is the most interesting star in the constellation, lying at top right. Even with the unaided eye, you can see that the star is double. The pair are faint – magnitudes +3.6 and +4.3 – and they aren't related. But each star itself is genuinely double, although you'll need a telescope to check this out.

The next-door star **Dabih** is also a double. The brighter member is a yellow star of magnitude +3.1; binoculars or a small telescope will reveal a blue companion at magnitude +6.

You'll need optical aid for the next beast in Capricornus – the globular

Damian Peach observed Jupiter on 3 June 2019, with the 1-m f/8 Ritchey–Chrétien reflector of the Chilescope Observatory and a ZWO ASI174MM camera.

cluster **M30**. This seventh-magnitude star cluster, about 27,000 light years away, was probably among the first objects to form in our Galaxy. And it's very pretty – so, if you're into astrophotography – point and shoot!

AUGUST'S OBJECT

The constellation of **Serpens** (the Serpent) has very little to write home about. But it does boast one gem, in the form of the **Eagle Nebula**. It's famed for a sensational image from the Hubble Space Telescope, revealing the glory of this star-forming region: the fantastic 'Pillars of Creation' that have gone down as a legend in cosmic sky sights.

The nebula (catalogued as M16) was discovered by Jean-Philippe Loys de Cheseaux in 1745. The gas cloud is 5700 light years away, and is home to hundreds of newborn stars. Compared to our ancient Sun, the Eagle is an infant on the cosmic scale: while our local star boasts an age of nearly 5 billion years, the toddlers of the Eagle Nebula are a mere 2 *million* years old.

Through binoculars, you'll easily spot the bright baby stars, but you'll need a telescope to view the nebulosity.

AUGUST'S TOPIC: PERSEIDS

Many people report to us that they see loads of shooting stars on their summer holidays – and are amazed when we observe: 'So you go on holiday in August?' But there's no mystery here. In the second week of August, the Earth runs into a stream of debris shed by Comet Swift-Tuttle. The specks of cosmic dust (about the size of coffee granules) smash into our atmosphere at a speed of 210,000 kilometres per hour,

and burn up in the flash of glory that we call a meteor.

Because of perspective, these shooting stars all appear to diverge from the same part of the sky – the *radiant* – which lies in the constellation Perseus. The Perseids are visible every year, but this August is a great time for viewing them as the show is not spoilt by moonlight. Stay up until after midnight on 12 August, for a free celestial fireworks display – with the bonus that August is much warmer than Bonfire Night!

AUGUST'S PICTURE

The Solar System's giant planet **Jupiter** appears in intricate detail in this image taken by Damian Peach with a telescope in the Atacama Desert, Chile. Jupiter is a delight to observe, as the coloured clouds in its atmosphere are ever changing. And that's also true of the Great Red Spot (lower centre). Once three times the size of the Earth, this huge storm has shrunk over the decades until it's now no wider than our planet.

SUNDAY	MONDAY	TUESDAY	WEDNESDAY	THURSDAY	FRIDAY	SATURDAY
1	2 Moon near the Pleiades (am); Saturn opposition	3 Moon near the Hyades, Aldebaran and the Pleiades	4	5	6	7
8 2.50 pm New Moon	9 Crescent Moon near Mercury, Mars and Regulus	10 Moon between Venus and Mars	11 Moon near Venus	12 Moon near Spica; Perseids	13 Perseids (am)	14
15 4.19 pm First Quarter Moon	16 Moon near Antares	17	18	19	20 Moon near Saturn; Jupiter opposition	21 Moon near Jupiter
22 1.02 pm Full Moon near Jupiter	23	24	25	26	27	28 Moon near the Pleiades
29 Moon between the Pleiades and the Hyades/Aldebaran	30 8.13 am Last Quarter Moon near Aldebaran and the Pleiades	31				

SPECIAL EVENTS

• **2 August, 3 am**: the Moon lies near the Pleiades.

• **2 August**: Saturn is opposite to the Sun in the sky, and closest to the Earth (see Planet Watch).

• **3 August, 3 am**: the Moon brushes the upper part of the Hyades, above Aldebaran, with the Pleiades above.

• **9 August**: look carefully to the right of brilliant Venus (preferably with binoculars) to pick out the young Moon. Below its narrow crescent are Mercury, with the rather fainter Mars and Regulus.

• **10 August**: the Moon lies between Venus (to the left) and the faint trio of Mercury, Mars and Regulus to the lower right (Chart 8a).

• **11 August**: a beautiful sight as the crescent Moon teams up with the Evening Star, Venus.

• **Night of 12/13 August**: maximum of the **Perseid meteor shower**. With the Moon setting before 10.30 pm, this is an excellent year for observing its abundance of fast, bright shooting stars.

• **20 August**: Jupiter is at its nearest this year and opposite the Sun (see Planet Watch).

• **21 August**: the Full Moon nuzzles up to second-brightest planet, Jupiter.

• **28 August**: the Pleiades lie to the left of the Moon.

• **29 August**: the Moon passes below the Pleiades, and above the Hyades and Aldebaran (Chart 8b).

• **30 August**: you'll find the Moon to the left of Aldebaran and the Hyades.

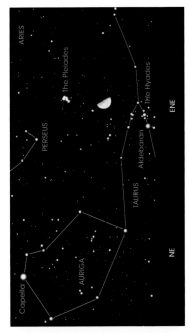

8a 10 August, 8.45 pm. The crescent Moon with Venus, Mars, Regulus and Mercury.

8b 29 August, 11.45 pm. The Moon with the Pleiades, Aldebaran and the Hyades.

• **Venus** is skulking low in the west after sunset, setting around 9.30 pm. At magnitude –4.0, only its brilliance makes it stand out against the bright twilight this month. **Mars** (magnitude +1.8) and **Mercury** (magnitude –0.5) are very low on the horizon to the lower right of Venus, and set around 9 pm.

• There's more planetary action in the south-east, as the Solar System's two giants both come closest to the Earth this year. First, there's **Saturn**, reaching its near point on 2 August, 'just' 1337 million kilometres away. In the middle of Capricornus, Saturn is visible all night and is at its maximum brightness of +0.2. Through a small telescope you can view its famous rings and the largest of its retinue of 82 moons.

• **Jupiter** blazes at magnitude –2.9 in Aquarius, again visible all night long. The giant planet passes nearest to us on 20 August, at a distance of 600 million kilometres. Even a pair of binoculars, held steadily, will show you Jupiter's four biggest moons, and a telescope reveals the cloud patterns on this gaseous planet.

• Faint **Neptune** (magnitude +7.8) lies on the other side of Aquarius, rising about 9 pm. **Uranus**, in Aries, shines at magnitude +5.7 and rises around 11 pm.

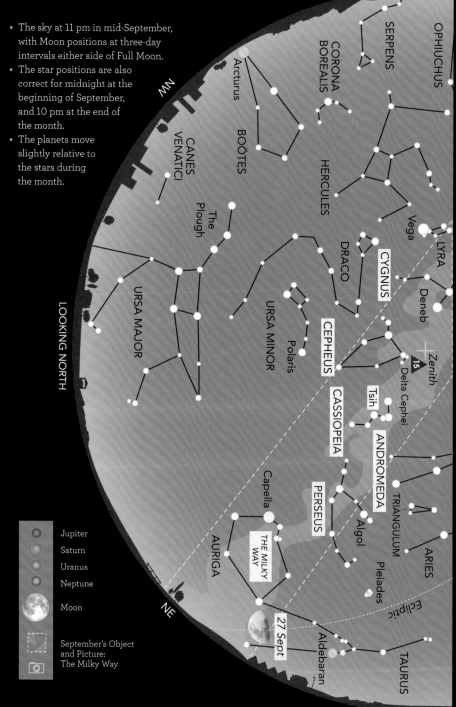

- The sky at 11 pm in mid-September, with Moon positions at three-day intervals either side of Full Moon.
- The star positions are also correct for midnight at the beginning of September, and 10 pm at the end of the month.
- The planets move slightly relative to the stars during the month.

WEST

OPHIUCHUS

SERPENS

CORONA BOREALIS

Arcturus

NW

CANES VENATICI

BOÖTES

HERCULES

The Plough

Vega

LYRA

DRACO

Deneb

CYGNUS

URSA MAJOR

URSA MINOR

Polaris

CEPHEUS

15

Zenith

LOOKING NORTH

Delta Cephei

Tsih

CASSIOPEIA

ANDROMEDA

Capella

PERSEUS

Algol

TRIANGULUM

ARIES

AURIGA

THE MILKY WAY

Pleiades

27 Sept

Aldebaran

Ecliptic

NE

TAURUS

Jupiter

Saturn

Uranus

Neptune

Moon

September's Object and Picture: The Milky Way

EAST

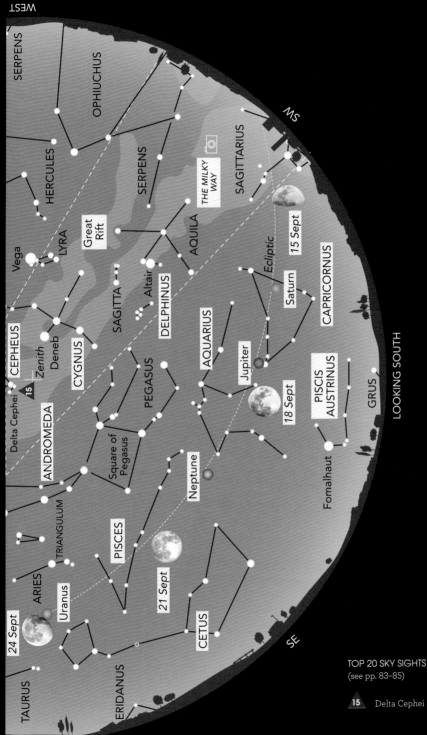

WEST

SERPENS

OPHIUCHUS

HERCULES

WS

SAGITTARIUS

SERPENS

THE MILKY WAY

AQUILA

Great Rift

LYRA

Vega

SAGITTA

Altair

DELPHINUS

15 Sept

CAPRICORNUS

Saturn

Ecliptic

CEPHEUS

Zenith

Deneb

CYGNUS

PEGASUS

AQUARIUS

Jupiter

18 Sept

PISCIS AUSTRINUS

GRUS

LOOKING SOUTH

Delta Cephei

15

ANDROMEDA

Square of Pegasus

Neptune

Fomalhaut

TRIANGULUM

PISCES

21 Sept

ARIES

Uranus

CETUS

24 Sept

TAURUS

ERIDANUS

SE

TOP 20 SKY SIGHTS
(see pp. 83–85)

15   Delta Cephei

EAST

The newly arriving autumn weather is heralded by a set of watery – but rather dim – constellations, sprawling over the southern skies. To the right of **Aquarius** (the Water Carrier), we have **Delphinus** (the Dolphin) and the strange Sea Goat (**Capricornus**). Below swims **Piscis Austrinus** (the Southern Fish), while a pair of Fishes (**Pisces**) and **Cetus** (the Sea Monster) lie to the left.

SEPTEMBER'S CONSTELLATION

Look almost overhead for a star pattern in the unmistakable shape of a 'W'. To the ancients, this constellation represented Queen **Cassiopeia** of Ethiopia, who ruled with her husband King **Cepheus**.

Cassiopeia misguidedly boasted that her daughter **Andromeda** was more beautiful than the sea nymphs. The sea god, Poseidon, was so incensed that he sent a ravaging monster (**Cetus**) to eat the young people of the country. It could only be appeased by the sacrifice of Andromeda – but she was rescued by the hero **Perseus**. These five major players are now all immortalised in the heavens.

Unusually, the central star in Cassiopeia is known by its Chinese name – **Tsih** (the Whip). This unstable star – some

OBSERVING TIP

It's best to view your favourite objects when they're well clear of the horizon. If you observe them low down, you're looking through a large thickness of the atmosphere – which is always shifting and turbulent. It's like trying to observe the outside world from the bottom of a swimming pool! This turbulence makes the stars appear to twinkle. Low-down planets also twinkle – although to a lesser extent, because they subtend tiny discs, and aren't so affected.

55,000 times brighter than the Sun – is spinning around at breakneck pace, flinging out streams of gas.

Cassiopeia has seen two supernovae, where an entire star has blown apart: one was seen by Danish astronomer Tycho Brahe (see January's Topic) in 1572, while the fireball from a second supernova (around 1660) is now the most prominent radio source in the sky, Cassiopeia A.

SEPTEMBER'S OBJECT

It's a stunning month for sweeping down the **Milky Way**, especially through binoculars. The stars look packed together, and you'll pick out star clusters and nebulae as you travel its length. These are all the more distant denizens of our local Galaxy, flattened into a band because we live within the plane of its disc. It's akin to seeing the overlapping streetlights of a distant city on Earth.

But you'll notice something else – there is a black gash between the stars. William Herschel, the first astronomer to map the Galaxy, thought that this was a hole in space. But now we know that the **Great Rift** in **Cygnus** is a dark swathe of sooty dust running along the disc of our Galaxy. Its material is poised to collapse under gravity, heat up, and – mixed with interstellar gas – create new generations of stars and planets. Proof that there is life in our old Galaxy yet!

SEPTEMBER'S TOPIC: THE BIG BANG

It's the biggest question of all: how did our Universe begin? These days, we don't have to rely on creation myths of what the gods got up to long ago. There's firm evidence that provides a definitive answer. First, the Universe is expanding – on the largest scales, galaxies are moving apart from each other. If you 'rewind the tape', you'll find that the expansion started 13.8 billion years ago – a measurement that has only been tied down in recent years. Secondly, the Universe is not completely cold – it's bathed in radiation at a temperature just 2.7 degrees above Absolute Zero, known as the microwave background.

These major clues – and other evidence – all point to the Universe being born in a blisteringly hot 'Big Bang', which caused space to expand. The microwave background is the remnant of this birth in fire, cooled down by the relentless expansion to a mere shadow of its former self. Current observations show that the Universe is not just expanding, but *accelerating* – which means that it's destined to die by ripping itself apart as its stars and galaxies fade away.

'The foreground was shot during twilight,' recalls Nick Bull, 'and the camera was left in position for two hours where I then took 15 × 13-second exposures at f/2.5 ISO 5000.' He used a Canon EOS 6D MkII camera and an Irix Firefly 15-mm lens, later stacking the night-time images in Sequator and blending them with the foreground in Photoshop.

SEPTEMBER'S PICTURE

A sight our ancestors may have venerated: the Milky Way rearing up over the ancient megaliths of Stonehenge. Its huge stones were shaped and erected around 4500 years ago, to celebrate the Winter Solstice. On that date, around 22 December, put yourself on the spot where photographer Nick Bull was standing, and you'd see the Sun set squarely behind Stonehenge. On this September night, he was able to image the grace and beauty of our Galaxy's glowing stars crowning the ancient stone circle.

SUNDAY	MONDAY	TUESDAY	WEDNESDAY	THURSDAY	FRIDAY	SATURDAY
			1	2	3 Moon near Castor and Pollux (am)	4
5 Venus near Spica	6	7 1.51 am New Moon	8	9 Moon near Venus	10 Moon near Venus	11
12 Moon near Antares	13 9.39 pm First Quarter Moon	14 Neptune opposition; Mercury E elongation	15	16 Moon near Saturn	17 Moon near Jupiter	18 Moon near Jupiter
19	20	21	22 Autumn Equinox	23	24	25 Moon near the Pleiades
26 Moon near Aldebaran and the Hyades	27	28	29 2.57 am Last Quarter Moon	30		

Hyades

SPECIAL EVENTS

- **9 September:** a thin crescent Moon lies to the right of Venus, with Mercury very low on the horizon (Chart 9a).
- **10 September:** the Evening Star forms a stunning duo with the crescent Moon (Chart 9a).
- **14 September:** Neptune is opposite to the Sun in the sky and at its closest to Earth this year (see Planet Watch).
- **16 September:** the Moon passes below Saturn, with Jupiter to the left (Chart 9b).
- **17 September:** you'll find Jupiter to the upper left of the Moon, while fainter Saturn lies to its upper right (Chart 9b).
- **18 September:** the Moon is to the left of giant planet Jupiter (Chart 9b).
- **22 September, 8.21 pm:** nights become shorter than days as the Sun moves south of the Equator at the Autumn Equinox.
- **25 September:** the Moon passes under the Pleiades.
- **26 September:** Aldebaran and the Hyades lie to the right of the Moon.

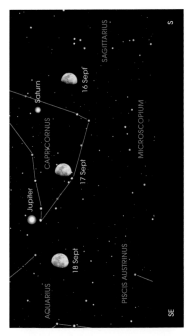

9a *9, 10 September, 7.45 pm. The crescent Moon with Venus, Spica and Mercury.*

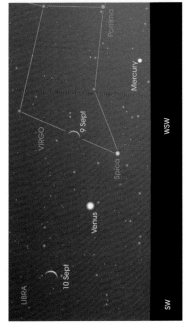

9b *16-18 September, 9 pm. The Moon with Saturn and Jupiter.*

Uranus

- The Evening Star hangs low in the west after sunset: **Venus** shines at a glorious magnitude –4.1, and sets around 8.30 pm. On 5 September it passes over Spica.

- You may catch **Mercury** (magnitude 0.0) to its lower right, deep in the twilight glow (Chart 9a): the innermost planet reaches maximum separation from the Sun on 14 September.

- The two largest planets – both lying in Capricornus – are livening up the rather dull starry sky to the south. Brilliant **Jupiter** (magnitude –2.8) sets around 4 am, while **Saturn** (to its right) glows at a dull magnitude +0.4 and sinks below the horizon about 2.30 am.

- **Neptune**, in Aquarius, is above the horizon all night long, and closest to the Earth on 14 September. But 'close'

is relative: the Solar System's most distant world then lies all of 4326 million kilometres away! Even though it's a giant planet, Neptune is not visible to the naked eye: at magnitude +7.8 you'll need binoculars or a telescope to see it.

- Its near twin in size, **Uranus**, lies in Aries and is just visible to the unaided eye at magnitude +5.7. The seventh planet rises about 9 pm.

- **Mars** is too close to the Sun to be visible this month.

SEPTEMBER'S PLANET WATCH

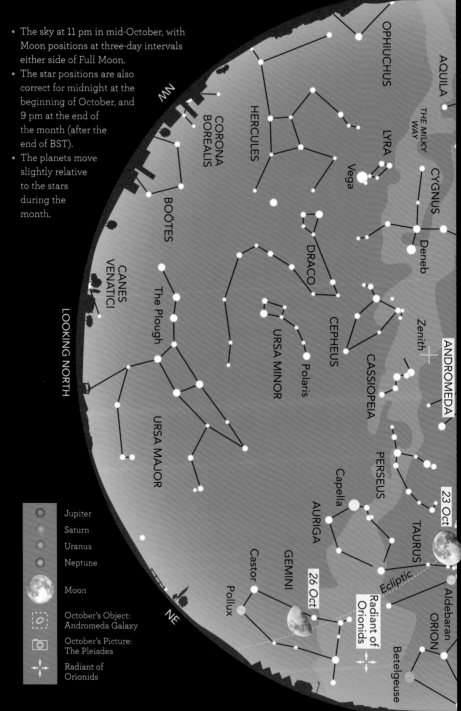

WEST

- The sky at 11 pm in mid-October, with Moon positions at three-day intervals either side of Full Moon.
- The star positions are also correct for midnight at the beginning of October, and 9 pm at the end of the month (after the end of BST).
- The planets move slightly relative to the stars during the month.

LOOKING NORTH

OPHIUCHUS

AQUILA

THE MILKY WAY

CYGNUS

LYRA

Vega

Deneb

CORONA BOREALIS

HERCULES

DRACO

CEPHEUS

Zenith

ANDROMEDA

BOÖTES

URSA MINOR

Polaris

CASSIOPEIA

CANES VENATICI

The Plough

URSA MAJOR

PERSEUS

Capella

23 Oct

TAURUS

AURIGA

Aldebaran

ORION

Castor

GEMINI

26 Oct

Radiant of Orionids

Ecliptic

Pollux

Betelgeuse

NE

○ Jupiter
○ Saturn
○ Uranus
○ Neptune

🌕 Moon

[O] October's Object: Andromeda Galaxy

📷 October's Picture: The Pleiades

✛ Radiant of Orionids

EAST

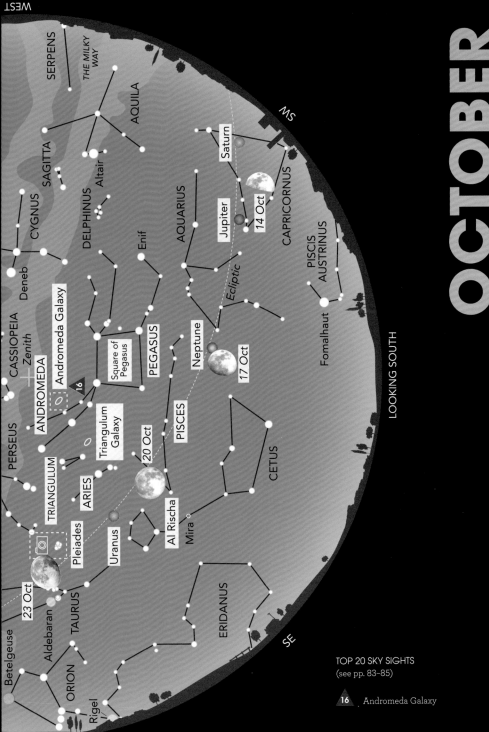

WEST

OCTOBER

THE MILKY WAY

SERPENS

AQUILA

SAGITTA

CYGNUS

DELPHINUS

Altair

Deneb

Enif

SW

Saturn

Jupiter

14 Oct

CAPRICORNUS

PISCIS AUSTRINUS

Fomalhaut

CASSIOPEIA

Zenith

ANDROMEDA

Andromeda Galaxy

16

PERSEUS

Square of Pegasus

PEGASUS

AQUARIUS

Ecliptic

Neptune

17 Oct

TRIANGULUM

Triangulum Galaxy

ARIES

20 Oct

PISCES

CETUS

LOOKING SOUTH

Pleiades

Uranus

Al Rischa

Mira

23 Oct

Aldebaran

TAURUS

ERIDANUS

SE

Betelgeuse

ORION

Rigel

EAST

TOP 20 SKY SIGHTS
(see pp. 83–85)

16   Andromeda Galaxy

The glories of October nights can best be described as 'subtle'. The barren **Square of Pegasus** dominates the southern sky, with **Andromeda** attached to his side. But the dull autumn constellations are already being faced down by the brilliant lights of winter, spearheaded by the beautiful star cluster of the **Pleiades**.

OCTOBER'S CONSTELLATION

Pisces is typical of the autumn constellations – faint and straggly, as it loops around the sky below **Pegasus**. Many ancient civilisations – from the Babylonians to the Egyptians and the early Christians – discerned a pair of fishes in this star pattern. To the ancient Greeks, they were the goddess Aphrodite and her son Eros, converted into piscine form and tied by a cord on their scaly tails, in order to escape from the monster Typhon.

The central star **Al Rischa** (whose name means 'cord' in Arabic) was discovered to be double, by William Herschel in 1779. The pair circle each other every 720 years, and currently appear very close together.

Pisces's main claim to fame is that it's the location of the Vernal Equinox – the point in the sky where the Sun crosses the celestial equator on its way from the southern to the northern hemisphere. That location is often called 'the first point of **Aries**', because it used to lie in the neighbouring constellation; but, as a result of Earth's wobbling on its axis (precession), it's now shifted into Pisces.

OCTOBER'S OBJECT

Take the advantage of autumn's newborn darkness to pick out our neighbour in the Universe, the **Andromeda Galaxy** (catalogued as M31 in Charles Messier's 1781 list of fuzzy patches).

Visible to the unaided eye, the Andromeda Galaxy covers an area four times bigger than the Full Moon. Like our Milky Way, it is a beautiful spiral shape, but – alas – it's presented to us almost edge-on. Even a small telescope won't reveal much detail.

The Andromeda Galaxy lies 2.5 million light years away: it's similar to the Milky Way, but larger. It also hosts two bright companion galaxies – just as our own Galaxy does – as well as a flotilla of orbiting dwarf galaxies.

OBSERVING TIP

The Andromeda Galaxy is often described as the furthest object 'easily visible to the unaided eye'. It can be a bit elusive, though – especially if you are suffering from light pollution. The trick is to memorise Andromeda's pattern of stars, and then to look slightly to the *side* of where you expect the galaxy to be. This technique – called 'averted vision' – causes the image to fall on the outer region of your retina, which is more sensitive to light than the central region that's evolved to discern fine details. You'll certainly need averted vision to eyeball Andromeda's fainter sibling, the Triangulum Galaxy, which lies even further away. The technique is also crucial when you want to observe the faintest nebulae or galaxies through a telescope.

From his home in Whittington, Shropshire, Pete Williamson caught this stunning view with a Takahashi 150-mm f/7.3 apochromatic refractor at the iTelescope.Net observatory in New Mexico. The total exposure was 60 minutes, and he processed the image in PixInsight 1.8.

Unlike other galaxies, which are receding from us in the expanding Universe, Andromeda is approaching the Milky Way. The two galaxies will merge in about 4 billion years' time. The pile-up will create a giant elliptical galaxy – nicknamed Milkomeda – devoid of gas and dominated by ancient red giant stars.

OCTOBER'S TOPIC: WHY DOES THE SUN SHINE?

Our local star seems to be an inexhaustible source of heat and light. For centuries a mystery, the source of the Sun's power was solved just over a century ago by British scientist Arthur Eddington, when he focused on the hydrogen gas in the Sun. Four hydrogen atoms can merge to make one helium atom. But the resulting atom is slightly lighter than four hydrogens: where does the missing mass go?

Eddington's 'eureka' moment was to invoke Albert Einstein's famous equation, $E=mc^2$, where 'E' is the energy that can be obtained from a mass 'm', and 'c' is the speed of light. When hydrogen turns to helium, the missing mass turns into the energy that powers the Sun.

At the Sun's core, conditions are extreme beyond our imagination. Gravity squeezes so tightly that the gas here is 70 times denser than gold. The temperature soars to 15.7 million degrees Celsius. Nuclear reactions are changing hydrogen into helium at such an incredible rate that the Sun is destroying 4 million tonnes of its matter *every second* – and converting it into pure energy.

That energy powers outwards through the Solar System, maintaining life on Earth for billions of years.

OCTOBER'S PICTURE

The small-but-perfectly-formed **Pleiades** star cluster is a leading feature of our winter skies. The 'Seven Sisters' visible to the naked eye comprise just a fraction of the 1000 stars making up the cluster. They are a delightful sight in binoculars, and magnificent when you view them through a wide-field telescope.

As Pete Williamson's image shows, the stars are hot and blue – fledglings on the celestial age scale – and surrounded by glorious nebulosity. Rather than material left over from the stars' birth, these glowing tendrils are part of an interstellar dust cloud which the Pleiades is crashing through.

OCTOBER'S CALENDAR

SUNDAY	MONDAY	TUESDAY	WEDNESDAY	THURSDAY	FRIDAY	SATURDAY
					1	2
3 Moon near Regulus (am)	4	5	6 12.05 pm New Moon	7	8	9 Crescent Moon near Venus
10 Moon near Antares	11 Moon near Antares	12	13 4.25 am First Quarter Moon, near Saturn	14 Moon near Jupiter and Saturn	15 Moon near Jupiter	16 Venus near Antares
17	18	19	20 3.56 pm Full Moon	21 Orionids	22 Orionids (am); Moon near the Pleiades	23 Moon near Aldebaran and the Hyades
24	25 Mercury W elongation	26	27 Moon near Castor and Pollux	28 9.05 pm Last Quarter Moon, near Praesepe	29 Venus E elongation	30 Moon near Regulus (am)
31 British Summer Time ends						

Orionid meteor

SPECIAL EVENTS

- **9 October:** look out for a stunning sight low in the south-west after sunset, as the narrow crescent Moon nuzzles up to Venus: the star to the left is Antares.
- **13 October:** to the left of the Moon are Saturn and then Jupiter (Chart 10a).
- **14 October:** the Moon lies below and between Jupiter (left) and Saturn (right) (Chart 10a).
- **15 October:** the brilliant 'star' near the Moon is the giant planet Jupiter (Chart 10a).
- **Night of 21/22 October:** maximum of the **Orionid meteor shower,** when debris from **Halley's Comet** smashes into Earth's atmosphere.

Bright moonlight spoils the display this year.
- **22 October:** the Moon lies near the Pleiades.
- **23 October:** the Moon passes over the Hyades and Aldebaran (Chart 10b).
- **31 October, 2 am:** the end of British Summer Time for this year, as clocks go backwards by an hour.

OCTOBER

66

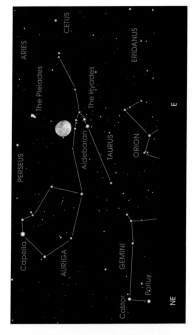

10a 13–15 October, 9 pm. The Moon passes Saturn and Jupiter.

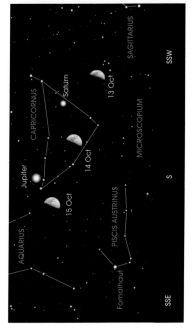

10b 23 October, 10 pm. The Moon with the Pleiades, Aldebaran and the Hyades.

• **Venus** – setting about 7.30 pm – is gradually brightening down in the south-west after sunset, from magnitude –4.2 at the start of October to –4.4 by the end of the month, as the planet draws closer to the Earth. The Evening Star passes above Antares on 16 October.

• Through a telescope, you can see Venus's shape slowly changing, like the phases of the Moon. The planet is half-lit (technically known as 'dichotomy') on 28 October, and then begins to shrink to a crescent On 29 October, Venus reaches its maximum separation from the Sun.

• In Capricornus, **Saturn** at magnitude +0.5 is setting around midnight. Its giant neighbour **Jupiter**, blazing at magnitude –2.6, sinks below the horizon about 2 am.

• Dim **Neptune** (magnitude +7.8) in Aquarius sets around 4.30 am. At magnitude +5.6, **Uranus** in Aries rises about 6.30 pm.

• **Mercury** is putting on its best morning appearance of the year. It appears low in the east before dawn in the middle of October, at magnitude +1.5. Throughout the month the innermost planet brightens, becoming easier to spot, and reaches magnitude –0.8 by the end of the month. Mercury is its maximum separation from the Sun on 25 October, when it rises at 5.25 pm.

• **Mars** is lost in the Sun's glare in October.

OCTOBER'S PLANET WATCH

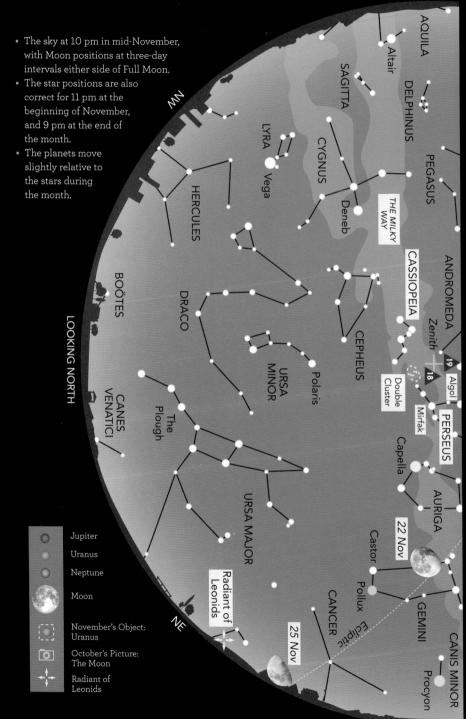

WEST

- The sky at 10 pm in mid-November, with Moon positions at three-day intervals either side of Full Moon.
- The star positions are also correct for 11 pm at the beginning of November, and 9 pm at the end of the month.
- The planets move slightly relative to the stars during the month.

AQUILA
Altair
DELPHINUS
SAGITTA
PEGASUS
CYGNUS
LYRA
Vega
Deneb
THE MILKY WAY
ANDROMEDA
CASSIOPEIA
Zenith
19
18
Algol
PERSEUS
Double Cluster
Mirfak
Capella
AURIGA

HERCULES
NW
BOÖTES
DRACO
CEPHEUS
URSA MINOR
Polaris

LOOKING NORTH

CANES VENATICI
The Plough
22 Nov
Castor
Pollux
GEMINI
URSA MAJOR
CANCER
25 Nov
CANIS MINOR
Procyon
Ecliptic

NE

Radiant of Leonids

Jupiter
Uranus
Neptune
Moon
November's Object: Uranus
October's Picture: The Moon
Radiant of Leonids

EAST

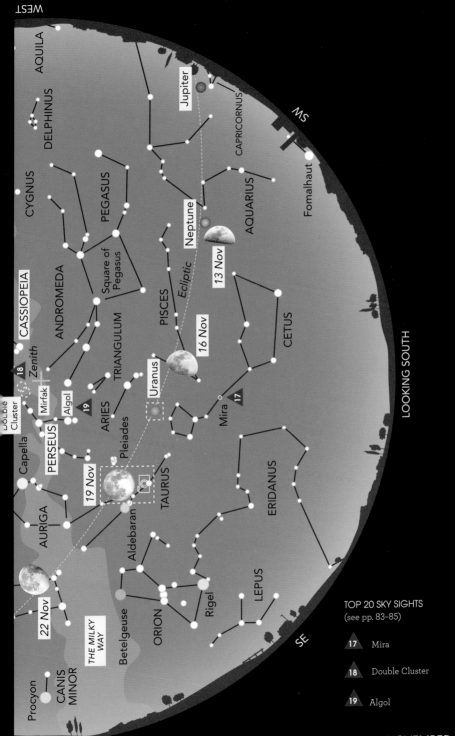

WEST

AQUILA

DELPHINUS

CYGNUS

CASSIOPEIA

Zenith

18

Double Cluster

Capella

Mirfak

PERSEUS

Algol

19

AURIGA

19 Nov

Procyon

CANIS MINOR

22 Nov

THE MILKY WAY

Betelgeuse

ORION

Rigel

LEPUS

Aldebaran

TAURUS

Pleiades

ARIES

TRIANGULUM

ANDROMEDA

Square of Pegasus

PEGASUS

Uranus

16 Nov

PISCES

Ecliptic

Neptune

13 Nov

Jupiter

MS

CAPRICORNUS

AQUARIUS

Fomalhaut

CETUS

Mira

17

ERIDANUS

LOOKING SOUTH

SE

NOVEMBER

TOP 20 SKY SIGHTS
(see pp. 83–85)

17   Mira

18   Double Cluster

19   Algol

EAST

The **Milky Way** rears overhead on these dark November nights, providing a stunning inside perspective on the huge Galaxy that is our home in space. Look carefully, and you can see that it's spangled with fuzzy glowing diadems. Even better, sweep the band of the Milky Way with binoculars or a small telescope, and these blurry jewels appear in their true guise: distant clusters of stars.

NOVEMBER'S CONSTELLATION

Perseus is one of the best-loved constellations in the northern night sky. It never sets from Britain, and is packed with celestial goodies. In legend, Perseus was the superhero who slew Medusa, the Gorgon. Its brightest star, **Mirfak** ('elbow' in Arabic), lies 510 light years away and is 5000 times more luminous than our Sun.

But the 'star' of Perseus has to be **Algol** (whose name stems from the Arabic *al-Ghul* – the Demon). It represents the eye of Medusa – and it winks. Its variations, first in 1783, are caused by a fainter star eclipsing the brighter one (see December's Object).

Another pair of gems is the **Double Cluster**, h and chi Persei. Visible to the unaided eye on the border with **Cassiopeia**, the duo is a sensational sight in binoculars. Some 7500 light years distant, the clusters are made of bright young blue stars. Both are a mere 13 million years old (compare this to our Sun, which has notched up 4.6 *billion* years so far!).

NOVEMBER'S OBJECT

If you're sharp-sighted and have extremely dark skies, you stand a chance of spotting **Uranus** – the most distant planet visible to the unaided eye – at its closest to Earth this year on 5 November. Discovered in 1781 by amateur astronomer William Herschel, Uranus was the first planet to be found since antiquity. The discovery doubled the size of our Solar System.

Four times the diameter of the Earth, Uranus has an odd claim to fame: it orbits the Sun on its side (probably as a result of a collision in its infancy). It has an encircling system of 13 faint narrow rings, far inferior to the spectacular edifices that girdle Saturn. Uranus also has a large family of moons: at the last count, 27.

The giant planet consists largely of a vast watery ocean surrounding a hot rocky core. The latest theories posit a hailstorm of diamonds dropping down through the water, to land in a sea of

OBSERVING TIP

With Christmas on the way, you may well be thinking of buying a telescope as a present for a budding stargazer. Beware! Unscrupulous websites and mail-order catalogues often advertise small telescopes that boast huge magnifications. This is 'empty magnification' – blowing up an image that the lens or mirror simply doesn't have the ability to get to grips with, so all you see is a bigger blur. The maximum magnification a telescope can actually provide is twice the diameter of the lens or mirror in millimetres. So if you see an advertisement for a 75-mm telescope, beware of any claims for a magnification greater than 150 times.

liquid diamond that wraps around the core. Though the Voyager spaceprobe revealed a bland, featureless world when it flew past Uranus in 1986, things are now hotting up as the planet's seasons change, with stormy clouds forming a bright cap around its north pole.

Mary McIntyre shot this helicopter transit on 10 January 2020, from Oxfordshire, using a Canon 1100D camera with a 300-mm zoom lens. Each exposure was 1/1250 second at f/5.6 and ISO 400. She aligned them with PIPP and combined them in Photoshop CS2, with processing in Lightroom and FastStone Image Viewer.

NOVEMBER'S TOPIC: CONSTELLATIONS

Perseus, our constellation of the month, highlights our obsession to 'join up the dots' in the sky and weave stories around them. One explanation is that the patterns acted as an *aide memoire* to ancient farming communities, as the seasons altered in step with annual change in the constellations as the Earth moved around the Sun.

The stars were also a great steer to navigation at sea. Ancient Minoan astronomers may have 'mapped' their legends onto the sky, so that sailors crossing the Mediterranean would associate key constellations with their traditional stories.

Not all the world saw the heavens through western eyes. The Chinese divided up the sky into a plethora of tiny constellations, containing three or four stars apiece. And the Aboriginal people of Australia, in their dark deserts, were so overwhelmed with stars that they made constellations out of dark patches where they couldn't see any stars!

NOVEMBER'S PICTURE

'Seize the moment' is a great maxim in life, and it's behind some of the most unusual astronomical photographs. Mary McIntyre was photographing the Full Moon in January 2020, as it was about to suffer a penumbral eclipse, when she saw an aircraft approaching. She changed her camera settings to take shorter exposures, and caught three silhouettes of her first helicopter 'transit' (here combined into a single shot). It was probably a Leonardo AW169 operated by the Children's Air Ambulance.

SUNDAY	MONDAY	TUESDAY	WEDNESDAY	THURSDAY	FRIDAY	SATURDAY
	1	2 Mercury near Spica (am)	3 Moon near Mercury (am)	4 9.14 pm New Moon	5 Uranus opposition	6
7 Moon near Venus	8 Moon near Venus	9	10 Mercury near Mars (am); Moon near Saturn	11 12.46 pm First Quarter Moon near Jupiter	12	13
14	15	16	17 Leonids	18 Leonids (am)	19 8.57 am Full Moon, near the Pleiades; partial lunar eclipse	20
21	22	23 Moon near Castor and Pollux	24	25	26 Moon near Regulus	27 12.27 pm Last Quarter Moon
28	29	30				

SPECIAL EVENTS

- **3 November, 6.30 am:** the narrow crescent Moon hangs above Mercury in the dawn twilight (binoculars will give a great view).
- **5 November:** Uranus is opposite to the Sun in the sky and is at its closest to Earth (see Planet Watch).
- **7 November:** the narrowest crescent Moon appears to the right of brilliant Venus, low in the south-western evening twilight (Chart 11a).
- **8 November:** a glorious evening tableau awaits us, with the crescent Moon next to the Evening Star (Chart 11a).
- **10 November, 6.30 am:** Mercury passes Mars in the dawn twilight (Chart 11b).
- **10 November:** the Moon lies below Saturn, with Jupiter to the left.
- **11 November:** the Moon passes below giant planet Jupiter, with fainter Saturn to the right.
- **Night of 17/18 November:** maximum of the Leonid meteor shower, but the display will be washed out by the brilliance of the nearly Full Moon.
- **19 November:** a total eclipse of the Moon is visible from the Americas, the Pacific and eastern Asia. The eclipse begins as the Moon is setting, as seen from the British Isles.
- **19 November:** the Moon lies below the Pleiades, and above Aldebaran and the Hyades.

SERPENS

SAGITTARIUS

Venus

7 Nov

OPHIUCHUS

8 Nov

SSW   SW

11a 7–8 November, 5.30 pm. Venus with the crescent Moon.

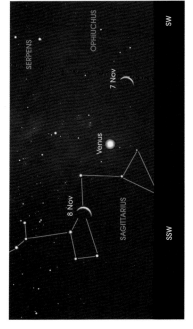

CORVUS

VIRGO

Spica

Mercury
Mars

ESE   SE

11b 10 November, 6.30 am. Mercury passes Mars, with Spica nearby.

• The Evening Star hangs low in the south-west. At a brilliant magnitude –4.5, **Venus** is setting at 6.30 pm.

• Well to the left, in the south, you'll find the second-brightest planet, giant **Jupiter** at magnitude –2.4, and between them the fainter **Saturn** (magnitude +0.7). Both of the Solar System's heavyweights lie in Capricornus, Saturn setting at around 9.30 pm and Jupiter about 11 pm.

• **Neptune**, in Aquarius, is a dim magnitude +7.8 and sinks below the horizon around 1.30 am.

• On 5 November, **Uranus** is at closest to the Earth this year, 2803 million kilometres away, and visible all night long. Even so, the planet is only just visible to the naked eye, at magnitude +5.6. At first sight, you'd be hard pushed to distinguish the planet from a number of stars of similar

brightness scattered around it in Pisces: check carefully with binoculars night after night, to spot Uranus gradually moving against the background stars.

• In the morning sky, **Mercury** is well on display at the beginning of November, rising in the east at 5.15 am and shining at magnitude –0.8. Initially it's near Spica, but the innermost planet gradually moves down

as the month progresses, disappearing into the twilight glow by mid-month

• On the way – the morning of 10 November to be precise – Mercury glides to the left of **Mars**, with the Red Planet at magnitude +1.6 appearing ten times fainter than the innermost world, with Spica to the upper right (Chart 11b).

• During November, Mars (rising at 6 am) is gradually ascending in the dawn sky.

NOVEMBER'S PLANET WATCH

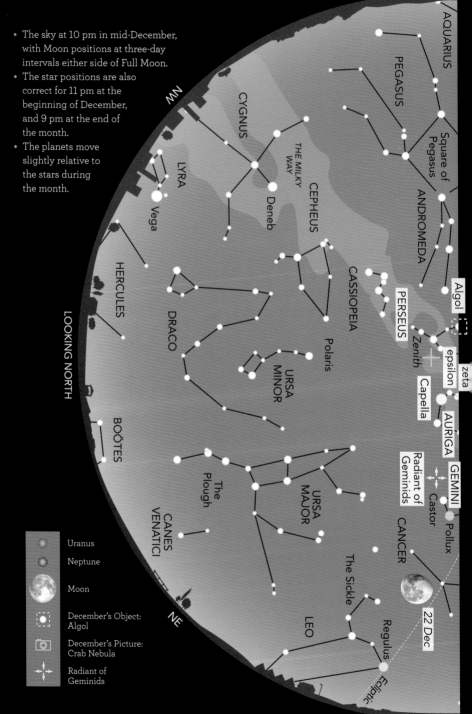

- The sky at 10 pm in mid-December, with Moon positions at three-day intervals either side of Full Moon.
- The star positions are also correct for 11 pm at the beginning of December, and 9 pm at the end of the month.
- The planets move slightly relative to the stars during the month.

WEST

AQUARIUS

PEGASUS

Square of Pegasus

ANDROMEDA

CYGNUS

THE MILKY WAY

Deneb

CEPHEUS

LYRA

Vega

CASSIOPEIA

PERSEUS

Algol

epsilon

zeta

Zenith

HERCULES

DRACO

Polaris

Capella

AURIGA

GEMINI

URSA MINOR

Castor

Pollux

Radiant of Geminids

BOÖTES

The Plough

URSA MAJOR

CANCER

CANES VENATICI

The Sickle

LEO

Regulus

22 Dec

NE

Ecliptic

LOOKING NORTH

Uranus

Neptune

Moon

December's Object: Algol

December's Picture: Crab Nebula

Radiant of Geminids

EAST

WEST

DECEMBER

WEST

PEGASUS

AQUARIUS

Square of
Pegasus

Neptune

10 Dec

Ecliptic

SW

ANDROMEDA

13 Dec

CETUS

TRIANGULUM

PISCES

ARIES

Uranus

PERSEUS

Algol

16 Dec

Mira

Gorgonea
Tertia

Pleiades

ERIDANUS

Zenith

epsilon

TAURUS

zeta

20

Capella

Aldebaran

ORION

LOOKING SOUTH

AURIGA

M38

M36

Rigel

LEPUS

M37

Crab
Nebula

Radiant of
Geminids

Betelgeuse

COLUMBA

Castor

19 Dec

Pollux

GEMINI

CANIS
MAJOR

CANCER

CANIS
MINOR

Procyon

THE MILKY
WAY

Sirius

Adhara

22 Dec

HYDRA

SE

EAST

TOP 20 SKY SIGHTS
(see pp. 83–85)

20   The Pleiades

DECEMBER   75

To end the year, there's a parade of planets after sunset and an impressive display of shooting stars, not to mention the brilliant constellations of winter: **Orion**, his hunting dogs **Canis Major** and **Canis Minor**, **Taurus** (the Bull), the hero twins of **Gemini**, and **Auriga** (this month's Constellation).

DECEMBER'S CONSTELLATION

Sparkling overhead, **Auriga** (the Charioteer) is named after the lame Greek hero Erichthonius, who invented the four-horse chariot. The constellation's roots date way back to the ancient Babylonians, who saw Auriga as a shepherd's crook.

Capella, the sixth-brightest star in the sky, means 'the little nanny goat', but there's nothing modest about this giant yellow star. In fact, it consists of two substantial stars, each ten times wider than the Sun and about 75 times brighter, orbiting more closely than the Earth circles the Sun. More controversially, this pair may be orbited by two faint red dwarf stars.

Nearby, you'll find a tiny triangle of stars known as the Kids (Haedi). Two are eclipsing binaries: stars that change in brightness because a companion passes in front. **Zeta** Aurigae is an orange star eclipsed every 972 days by a blue partner.

OBSERVING TIP

Venus is at its glorious best this month. Through a small telescope, you'll be able to make out its crescent shape. But don't wait for the sky to get totally dark. Seen against a black sky, the cloud-wreathed world is so brilliant it's difficult to make out any details. You're best off viewing Venus soon after the Sun has set, when the Evening Star first becomes visible in the twilight glow. Through a telescope, the planet then appears less dazzling against a pale blue sky.

Epsilon Aurigae (also known as Almaaz) is a weirdo. Every 27 years, it suffers a two-year long eclipse, caused by a dark disc of material almost as big as the orbit of Jupiter. No two eclipses are the same: and there are tantalising hints of giant proto-planets within the disc.

Also, bring out those binoculars (better still, a small telescope) – to sweep within the 'body' of the Charioteer to find three very pretty open star clusters, **M36**, **M37** and **M38**.

DECEMBER'S OBJECT

The star **Algol**, in the constellation **Perseus**, represents the head of the dreadful Gorgon Medusa. In Arabic, its name means 'the Demon'. Watch Algol carefully and you'll see why. Every 2 days 21 hours, Algol dims in brightness for several hours – to become as faint as the star lying to its lower right (**Gorgonea Tertia**).

In 1783, an 18-year-old profoundly deaf amateur astronomer, from York – John Goodricke – discovered Algol's regular changes, and proposed that the star was orbited by a large dark planet that periodically blocks off some of its light. We now know that Algol' does indeed have a dim companion blocking its brilliant light, but it's a fainter star, rather than a planet. While the main star is 180 times more luminous than the Sun, and a searing blue-white in colour, the dimmer red companion is only seven times brighter than our local star.

DECEMBER'S TOPIC: PULSARS

It was a signal so weird that the discoverers labelled it 'LGM-1'; perhaps the first communication from 'Little Green Men'. The radio astronomers at Cambridge, in 1967, had detected a regular stream of radio pulses, once every 1.337 seconds. It wasn't coming from an alien intelligence, however, but something almost as outlandish: a pulsar.

A pulsar is the collapsed core of a massive star that has exploded as a supernova. It's composed entirely of tiny subatomic particles called neutrons, so tightly packed that a pulsar (also called a neutron star) contains as much matter as the Sun, in a ball no bigger than London!

A pinhead of its material would weigh as much as a fully laden supertanker, and its gravity is so strong you'd expend more effort climbing a 1-centimetre bump than in ascending Mount Everest on Earth. A typical pulsar has a fearsome magnetic field, a thousand billion times stronger than Earth's magnetism. As it spins round, beams of radiation sweep around like a lighthouse beacon, creating the radio pulses we detect.

The energised magnetic cocoon around a young powerful pulsar can shine with an eerie blue glow, seen in all its glory in the Crab Nebula (see Picture).

DECEMBER'S PICTURE

With a moderate telescope, you can spot a strange twisted patch of light in the sky – the **Crab Nebula** – just above the 'lower horn' of **Taurus** (the Bull). Here, Chinese astronomers in AD 1054 witnessed the appearance of a brilliant 'guest star'. Visible in daylight for 23 days, the supernova remained in the night sky for nearly two years.

To lay bare the complex details of the Crab Nebula, Pete Williamson employed remote observing: he used the powerful Faulkes North Telescope on the summit of Haleakala in Hawaii, while sitting at home in Shropshire! The instrument is a 2-m Ritchey–Chrétien reflector, and Pete took 16 × 90-second exposures through four coloured filters (R, G, B and H-alpha), with a total exposure time of 24 minutes.

In the 19th century, the Third Earl of Rosse looked closely at the remains of this exploded star with his powerful telescope, sited in the central bogs of Ireland. It reminded him of a crab's pincers, hence the nebula's popular name.

The expanding debris now measures 11 light years across, and shines at magnitude +8.4. In Pete Williamson's evocative image, the reddish filaments are strands of hot gas blown out by the explosion. The central bluish glow is created by electrons whirling around in the magnetism of the pulsar (see Topic), visible as the lower of the two stars right in the nebula's core.

DECEMBER'S CALENDAR

SUNDAY	MONDAY	TUESDAY	WEDNESDAY	THURSDAY	FRIDAY	SATURDAY
			1 Moon near Spica (am)	2	3	4 7:43 am New Moon; total solar eclipse
5	6 Moon near Venus	7 Venus at maximum brightness; Moon near Venus	8 Moon near Venus	9 Moon near Jupiter	10	11 1.35 am First Quarter Moon
12	13 Geminids	14 Geminids (am)	15	16 Moon near the Pleiades	17 Moon near Aldebaran and the Hyades	18
19 4.35 am Full Moon	20 Moon near Castor and Pollux	21 Winter Solstice; Moon near Castor and Pollux	22	23 Moon near Regulus	24	25
26	27 Mars near Antares (am); 2.23 am Last Quarter Moon	28 Mars near Antares (am); Moon near Spica (am)	29	30	31 Moon near Mars (am)	

SPECIAL EVENTS

- **4 December:** a total eclipse of the Sun is visible from Antarctica. Nothing will be seen from the British Isles.
- **6 December:** look to the lower right of brilliant Venus to spot the narrow crescent Moon (Chart 12a).
- **7 December:** Venus reaches its brightest this year, at maximum −4.7. The Evening Star forms a stunning duo with the crescent Moon, in the south-west after sunset (Chart 12a).
- **8 December:** the Moon hangs between Saturn and Jupiter, with Venus well to the right (Chart 12a).
- **9 December:** giant planet Jupiter lies to the upper right of the Moon (Chart 12a).
- **Night of 13/14 December:** look out for the bright, slow shooting stars of the **Geminid meteor shower**, which – unusually – are debris not from a comet, but from an asteroid, called Phaethon. You'll get the best views in the wee small hours, after the Moon has set.
- **16 December:** the Moon passes under the Pleiades, with Aldebaran and the Hyades to the lower left.
- **17 December:** Aldebaran and the Hyades lie to the right of the Moon.
- **21 December, 3.59 pm:** the Winter Solstice – the shortest day and longest night.
- **31 December, 7 am:** low in the south-east, the narrow crescent Moon hangs to the upper right of Mars, with Antares below.

78   DECEMBER

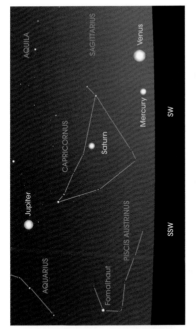

12a 6–9 December, 5.30 pm. The Moon passes Venus, Saturn and Jupiter.

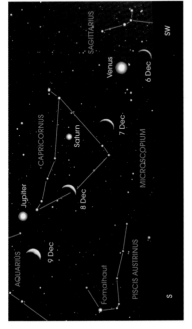

12b 31 December, 5 pm. Venus and Mercury, with Saturn and Jupiter.

• Over in the south-west, there's a line of three bright planets: Venus to the right, Saturn in the middle and Jupiter on the left. At the start of December, Venus is steaming towards the other two, but just after mid-month the Evening Star changes direction and heads back downwards again. Here's more detail on each of these three worlds.

• **Venus** starts the month at magnitude −4.6 (peaking at a brilliant −4.7 on 7 December) but fades to magnitude −4.3 by the end of December. Through a telescope, or even binoculars held steadily, you can see the planet shrink dramatically to a narrow crescent.

• At the start of December the Evening Star is setting at 6.30 pm, but by the end of the month it sinks below the horizon as early as 5.20 pm. During the last few days of December, you may catch

Mercury to the lower left of Venus, setting at the same time and 30 times fainter at magnitude −0.7 (Chart 12b).

• **Saturn** lies in Capricornus all month, shining at magnitude +0.7 and setting around 7.30 pm. Its larger sibling **Jupiter** is at a magnificent magnitude −2.2 and sinks below the horizon about 9 pm, moving from Capricornus to Aquarius around mid-month.

• To the other side of Aquarius, dim **Neptune** glows at magnitude +7.9 and sets about 11.30 pm. **Uranus** (magnitude +5.7) in Aries is setting around 4.30 am.

• You'll find **Mars** low in the morning twilight, rising in the south-east at 6 am and shining at magnitude +1.6. During December, the Red Planet moves from Libra, through Scorpius and into Ophiuchus. On the mornings of 27 and 28 December, Mars passes above Antares.

Can you see the planets? We're amazed when people ask us that question: some of our cosmic neighbours are the brightest objects in the night sky after the Moon. As they're so close, you can watch them getting up to their antics from night to night. And planetary debris – leftovers from the birth of the Solar System – can light up our skies as glowing comets and the celestial fireworks of a meteor shower.

THE SUN-HUGGERS

Mercury and Venus orbit the Sun more closely than our own planet, so they never seem to stray far from our local star: you can spot them in the west after sunset, or the east before dawn, but never all night long. At *elongation*, the planet is at its greatest separation from the Sun, though – as you can see in the diagram (right) – that's not when the planet is at its brightest. Through a telescope, Mercury and Venus (technically known as the *inferior planets*) show phases like the Moon – from a thin crescent to a full globe – as they orbit the Sun.

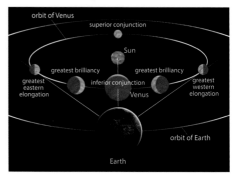

Venus (and Mercury) show phases like the Moon as they orbit the Sun.

Mercury

The innermost planet appears in the evening sky in January, makes its best appearance in April–May, and then reappears in the dusk sky during last few days of the year (its evening appearance in August–September is largely lost in the bright twilight). Mercury is low in the dawn twilight at its February–March and July apparitions; it's best seen before dawn in October–November.

Venus

Though you'll catch Venus in the morning sky in January, it lurks behind the Sun through to the middle of April. From then till the end of the year, Venus is a permanent fixture of the western dusk twilight in the evening sky, as the Evening Star. It reaches its greatest separation from the Sun in October, and maximum brightness on **7 December.**

Maximum elongations of Mercury in 2021	
Date	Separation
24 January	19° east
6 March	27° west
17 May	22° east
4 July	22° west
14 September	27° east
25 November	18° west

Maximum elongation of Venus in 2021	
Date	Separation
29 October	47° east

WORLDS BEYOND

A planet orbiting the Sun beyond the Earth (known in the jargon as a *superior planet*) is visible at all times of night, as we look outwards into the Solar System. It lies due south at midnight when the Sun, the Earth and the planet are all in line – a time known as *opposition* (see the diagram, right). Around this time the Earth lies nearest to the planet, although the date of closest approach (and the planet's maximum brightness) may differ by a few days because the planets' orbits are not circular.

Mars

The Red Planet hangs around in the evening sky for most of the year, gradually fading as its distance from the Earth increases. Disappearing from the evening sky in August, and passing behind the Sun on **8 October**, Mars reappears in the dawn twilight in November.

● Where to find Mars	
Early January	Pisces
Mid-January to mid-February	Aries
Late February to mid-April	Taurus
Late April to early June	Gemini
Mid-June to early July	Cancer
Mid- to late July	Leo
November to early December	Libra
Mid-December	Scorpius
Late December	Ophiuchus

Jupiter

The giant planet starts the year low in the evening sky, sinking into the sunset by the end of January. It reappears in the morning sky at the end of February, still in Capricornus where it remains until May when Jupiter moves into Aquarius. Reaching opposition on **20 August**,

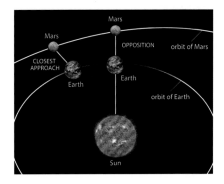

Mars (and the outer planets) line up with the Sun and Earth at opposition, but they are brightest at their point of closest approach.

Jupiter moves back into Capricornus in September, and is visible in the evening sky until the end of the year, when it treks into Aquarius again.

Saturn

You'll find the ringed planet near Jupiter throughout the year. In January, it disappears into the twilight glow, to re-emerge at the end of February in the dawn sky. Saturn is at opposition on **2 August**, and you'll then see it in the evening sky until the close of 2021. It resides in Capricornus all year.

Uranus

Just perceptible to the naked eye, Uranus lies in Aries all year. Up until May, the seventh planet is visible in the evening sky. It emerges from the Sun's glow in the morning sky in July. Uranus is at opposition on **5 November**.

Neptune

The most distant planet lies in Aquarius throughout the year, and is at opposition on **14 September**. Neptune can be seen (though only through binoculars or a telescope) in January and February and then from late April until the end of the year.

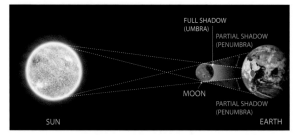

Where the dark central part (the umbra) of the Moon's shadow reaches the Earth, we are treated to a total solar eclipse. If the shadow doesn't quite reach the ground, we see an annular eclipse. People located within the penumbra observe a partial eclipse.

SOLAR ECLIPSES

On **10 June**, anyone who's in a narrow strip of the Earth's surface – from north-east Canada via the North Pole to eastern Siberia – will be treated to an annular eclipse of the Sun. The British Isles will experience a partial solar eclipse: from the south-east of England, the Moon covers 19 per cent of the Sun, rising to 35 per cent as viewed from Shetland.

On **4 December**, a total eclipse of the Sun is visible from West Antarctica and adjacent regions of the Southern Ocean. Nothing is visible from Britain.

LUNAR ECLIPSES

A total lunar eclipse on **26 May** will be seen from the Pacific Ocean and the countries of the Pacific Rim, but not from the British Isles.

On **19 November**, a large partial eclipse of the Moon is visible from the Americas, the Pacific and eastern Asia. As seen from Britain, the eclipse begins as the Moon is setting.

METEOR SHOWERS

Shooting stars, or *meteors*, are tiny specks of interplanetary dust, burning up in the Earth's atmosphere. At certain times of year, Earth passes through a stream of debris (usually left by a comet) and we see a *meteor shower*. The meteors appear to emanate from a point in the sky known as the *radiant*. Most showers

Table of meteor showers	
Meteor shower	Date of maximum
Quadrantids	3/4 January
Lyrids	21/22 April
Eta Aquarids	5/6 May
Perseids	12/13 August
Orionids	21/22 October
Leonids	17/18 November
Geminids	13/14 December

are known by the constellation in which the radiant lies.

It's fun and rewarding to hold a meteor party. Note the location, cloud cover, the time and brightness of each meteor and its direction through the stars – along with any persistent afterglow (train).

COMETS

Comets are dirty snowballs from the outer Solar System. If they fall towards the Sun, its heat evaporates their ices to produce a gaseous head (*coma*) and sometimes dramatic tails. Although some comets are visible to the naked eye, use binoculars to reveal stunning details in the coma and the tail.

Hundreds of comets move round the Sun in small orbits. But many more don't return for thousands or even millions of years. Most comets are now discovered in professional surveys of the sky, but a few are still found by dedicated amateur astronomers. Watch out in case a brilliant new comet puts in a surprise appearance!

We've always had our favourite sights in the night sky: and here they are in a season-by-season summary. It doesn't matter if you're a complete beginner, finding your way around the heavens with the unaided eye ◉ or binoculars ♙; or if you're a seasoned stargazer, with a moderate telescope ↘. There's something here for everyone.

Each sky sight comes with a brief description, and a guide as to how you can best see it. Many of the most delectable objects are faint, so avoid moonlight when you go out spotting. Most of all, enjoy!

SPRING

Praesepe ◉ ♙ ↘

Constellation: Cancer
Star Chart/Key: March; **5**
Type/Distance: Star cluster; 600 light years
Magnitude: +3.7
A fuzzy patch to the unaided eye; a telescope reveals many of its 1000 stars.

M81 and M82 ♙ ↘

Constellation: Ursa Major
Star Chart/Key: March; **6**
Type/Distance: Galaxies; 12 million light years
Magnitude: +6.9 (M81); +8.4 (M82)
A pair of interacting galaxies: the spiral M81 appears as an oval blur, and the starburst M82 as a streak of light.

The Plough

The Plough ◉

Constellation: Ursa Major
Star Chart/Key: April; **7**
Type/Distance: Asterism; 82–123 light years
Magnitude: Stars are roughly magnitude +2
The seven brightest stars of the Great Bear form a large saucepan shape, called 'the Plough'.

Mizar and Alcor ◉ ♙ ↘

Constellation: Ursa Major
Star Chart/Key: April; **8**
Type/Distance: Double star; 83 & 82 light years
Magnitude: +2.3 (Mizar); +4.0 (Alcor)
The sky's classic double star, easily separated by the unaided eye: a telescope reveals Mizar itself is a close double.

Virgo Cluster ♙ (difficult) ↘

Constellation: Virgo
Star Chart/Key: May; **9**
Type/Distance: Galaxy cluster; 54 million light years
Magnitude: Galaxies range from magnitude +9.4 downwards
Huge cluster of 2000 galaxies, best seen through moderate to large telescopes.

SUMMER

Antares ◉ ♙ ↘

Constellation: Scorpius
Star Chart/Key: June; **10**
Type/Distance: Double star; 550 light years
Magnitude: +0.96
Bright red star close to the horizon. You can spot a faint green companion with a telescope.

M13 👁 🔭 📷

Constellation: Hercules
Star Chart/Key: June; 🔺11
Type/Distance: Star cluster; 22,200 light years
Magnitude: +5.8
A faint blur to the naked eye, this ancient globular cluster is a delight seen through binoculars or a telescope. It boasts nearly a million stars.

Lagoon and Trifid Nebulae 👁 🔭 📷

Constellation: Sagittarius
Star Chart/Key: July; 🔺12
Type/Distance: Nebulae; 4000 light years (Lagoon); 5200 (Trifid)
Magnitude: +6.0 (Lagoon); +7.0 (Trifid)
While the Lagoon Nebula is just visible to the unaided eye, you'll need binoculars or a telescope to spot the Trifid. The two are in the same telescope field of view, and present a stunning photo opportunity.

Albireo 👁 🔭 📷

Constellation: Cygnus
Star Chart/Key: August; 🔺13
Type/Distance: Double star; 415 light years
Magnitude: Albireo A: +3.2; Albireo B: +5.1
Good binoculars reveal Albireo as being double. But you'll need a small telescope to appreciate its full glory. The brighter star appears golden; its companion shines piercing sapphire. It is the most beautiful double star in the sky.

Dumbbell Nebula 🔭 📷

Constellation: Vulpecula
Star Chart/Key: August; 🔺14
Type/Distance: Planetary nebula; 1300 light years
Magnitude: +7.5

Dumbbell Nebula

Andromeda Galaxy

Visible through binoculars, and a lovely sight through a small/medium telescope, this is a dying star that has puffed off its atmosphere into space.

AUTUMN

Delta Cephei 👁 🔭

Constellation: Cepheus
Star Chart/Key: September; 🔺15
Type/Distance: Variable star; 890 light years
Magnitude: +3.5 to +4.4, varying over 5 days 9 hours
The classic variable star, Delta Cephei is chief of the Cepheids – stars that allow us to measure distances in the Universe (their variability time is coupled to their intrinsic luminosity). Visible to the unaided eye, but you'll need binoculars for serious observations.

Andromeda Galaxy 👁 🔭 📷

Constellation: Andromeda
Star Chart/Key: October; 🔺16
Type/Distance: Galaxy; 2.5 million light years
Magnitude: +3.4
The nearest major galaxy to our own, the Andromeda Galaxy is easily visible to the unaided eye in unpolluted skies. Four times the width of the Full Moon, it's a great telescopic object and photographic target.

Mira 👁 🔭 📷

Constellation: Cetus
Star Chart/Key: November; 🔺17
Type/Distance: Variable star; 300 light years
Magnitude: +3.5 to +10.1 over 332 days, although maxima and minima may vary.

Nicknamed 'the Wonderful', this distended red giant star is alarmingly variable as it swells and shrinks. At its brightest, Mira is a naked-eye object; binoculars may catch it at minimum; but you need a telescope to monitor this star. Its behaviour is unpredictable, and it's important to keep logging it.

Double Cluster

Constellation: Perseus
Star Chart/Key: November; **18**
Type/Distance: Star clusters; 7500 light years
Magnitude: +3.7 and +3.8
A lovely sight to the unaided eye, these stunning young star clusters are sensational through binoculars or a small telescope. They're a great photographic target.

Algol

Constellation: Perseus
Star Chart/Key: November; **19**
Type/Distance: Variable star; 90 light years
Magnitude: +2.1 to +3.4 over 2 days 21 hours
Like Mira, Algol is a variable star, but not an intrinsic one. It's an 'eclipsing binary' – its brightness falls when a fainter companion star periodically passes in front of the main star. It's easily monitored by the eye, binoculars or a telescope.

WINTER

Pleiades

Constellation: Taurus
Star Chart/Key: December; **20**
Type/Distance: Star cluster; 444 light years
Magnitude: Stars range from magnitude +2.9 downwards
To the naked eye, most people can see six stars in the cluster, but it can rise to 14 for the keen-sighted. In binoculars or a telescope, they are a must-see. Astronomers have observed 1000 stars in the Pleiades.

Orion Nebula

Constellation: Orion
Star Chart/Key: January; **1**
Type/Distance: Nebula; 1300 light years
Magnitude: +4.0

A striking sight even to the unaided eye, the Orion Nebula – a star-forming region 24 light years across – hangs just below Orion's belt. Through binoculars or a small telescope, it is staggering. A photographic must!

Betelgeuse

Constellation: Orion
Star Chart/Key: January; **2**
Type/Distance: Variable star; 720 light years
Magnitude: 0.0 – +1.3
Even with the unaided eye, you can see that Betelgeuse is slightly variable over months, as the red giant star billows in and out.

M35

Constellation: Gemini
Star Chart/Key: February; **3**
Type/Distance: Star cluster; 2800 light years
Magnitude: +5.3
Just visible to the unaided eye, this cluster of around 2000 stars is a lovely sight through a small telescope.

Sirius

Constellation: Canis Major
Star Chart/Key: February; **4**
Type/Distance: Double star; 8.6 light years
Magnitude: –1.47
You can't miss the Dog Star. It's the brightest star in the sky! But you'll need a 150-mm reflecting telescope (preferably bigger) to pick out its +8.44 magnitude companion – a white dwarf nicknamed 'the Pup'.

Pleiades

CHOOSING & USING BINOCULARS

BY ROBIN SCAGELL

Many books advise beginners to astronomy to start by using binoculars. Not only are they good value, but they can give wonderful views of the heavens as well as being handy by day for many leisure activities. Compared with telescopes they're simple to use, and are often portable enough to be taken anywhere on the off-chance of getting a good sky.

Of course, they have limitations. They usually have a fixed and rather low magnification and their very portability means that they can be hard to hold steady. But as long as you accept that they can't do everything, they are a great buy, and virtually every stargazer has binoculars as part of their instrument collection.

CHOOSE YOUR BINOCULARS

You don't need to spend a fortune on top-quality binoculars for astronomy. Avoid the very cheapest, which almost certainly will be of limited optical quality and are likely to go out of line at the slightest knock, giving double vision which can't be corrected. But unless you also want to use them for a variety of other purposes, such as on a boat or when bird-watching, you don't need them to be extensively ruggedised. Few astronomers observe in the rain!

The choice of size is really important. Start by considering the most useful all-purpose size for astronomy, 10 × 50s, which have a magnification of 10 and objective lenses (the ones at the front) 50 mm across. It's the objective size, or *aperture*, that affects the weight and bulk of the binoculars, and therefore the length of time you can easily hold them up to the sky. There's no substitute for testing them in a shop. If your arms begin to ache after a minute or two of holding them, think about a smaller size, such as 42 mm, but don't go much smaller than that for astronomy or lack of light will start to become an issue.

If you just want general-purpose binoculars that will show you nice views of starry skies, you could stick to a magnification of 7 or 8. But to be able to see some galaxies and deep-sky objects, you'll need a magnification of 10 or more, so 12 × 42 is a good combination of light weight and reasonable magnification.

If you go for the larger 50 mm size, you could choose a magnification of 10,

A selection of binocular sizes. Left to right (front): 10 × 35, 10 × 30 image stabilised, 8 × 42, 10 × 50, (back) 20 × 60, 15 × 70. All except the 10 × 30s use Porro prisms to shorten the barrel length. The 10 × 30s use roof prisms, which are more compact.

12 or 16. But remember that the more you magnify for a given aperture, the more the available light is spread out, so the dimmer the view. One possibility is to go for binoculars with a range of magnifications, with zoom eyepieces. If so, beware the cheap ones, often advertised online or in newspaper ads that may claim they are perfect for astronomy and with a ridiculously wide range. A top magnification of 24 or so is more than adequate. Zoom mechanisms and optics are much more fiddly than fixed magnifications, and can easily be disturbed unless very well made. And you will probably find that you rarely use them at their maximum power for astronomy, as they are much harder to hold steady at high magnification.

This raises the matter of supporting binoculars so as to avoid tired arms and shaky views. A tripod is a possibility, but a monopod is often more convenient as its single extending leg won't get in your way as much when viewing objects high up.

Or to keep the view steady, you could go for image-stabilised (IS) binoculars. These have active optics which almost magically calm a jittery image when you press a button. My own Canon 10 × 30 IS are my favourite binoculars for their lightness and steadiness. Only when I can't see a faint object do I turn to 10 × 50s or a more powerful instrument.

Many keen amateurs own higher-power binoculars for such occasions. A very popular size is 15 × 70, followed by 20 × 60. Although these are too large for convenient use, they do give excellent views of the brighter and larger deep-sky objects and are available at surprisingly low cost.

The easy way to view objects high in the sky with large binoculars, using a lounger and monopod. This takes the weight off your arms, yet allows freedom of movement.

WHAT CAN YOU SEE?

Even in light-polluted city skies, binoculars have their uses. They will show you stars and even constellations that you just can't see with the naked eye alone. The Moon changes from being a mottled disc to a three-dimensional world on which you can clearly see craters, mountain chains, the ancient 'seas' of solidified lava and many other features. You can easily identify many of the features shown on Moon maps, and learn your way around our nearest neighbour.

The Sun can also hold surprises. However, you need to take particular care when observing it because of its brightness. The only safe way is to fit solar filters over one or both objective lenses. You can buy such ready-made filters but many people make their own from suitable sheet material such as Baader AstroSolar® film. The crucial thing is to make sure there's no chance of them falling off, or letting through a chink of light. Alternatively, project the Sun's image onto white card, making sure not to let it drift out of the field of view as the Sun's heat could damage the interior of the binoculars.

The Moon is a great target for study with binoculars. First Quarter is an ideal time, as the low Sun angle along the terminator makes the lunar relief very clear.

Once safely filtered, you can view not only the occasional partial solar eclipses, such as that on 10 June this year (see p. 42), but also any large sunspots. Currently the Sun is at a low state of activity, but a maximum of activity is expected sometime between 2023 and 2026. At that time, sunspots should be easily visible with binoculars. You might also want to travel to view a total solar eclipse, although the next readily available one won't be until April 2023, visible from the Indonesian Archipelago. There's another in April 2024, visible from the US. Binoculars are great for observing the total phase.

Typical binoculars don't have enough magnification to show any detail on the planets, but the phase of Venus is evident, particularly when it's close to Earth as it will be in the evening sky right at the end of this year, showing a fine crescent phase. The moons of Jupiter are also easy to spot, and you can watch their movements from night to night.

DARK-SKY VIEWS

But it's in a good, dark country sky that binoculars really come into their own. So many stars become visible in the field of view that you can easily get lost. Many newcomers find it hard to work out what they are looking at, because suddenly stars that look insignificant become bright. You need to get used to this brightness increase by choosing a group of stars that are close together and comparing the naked-eye view with what you see through the binoculars. The Pleiades star cluster (see p. 65), visible in evening skies between October and April, is perfect for this, but in summer try Vega, which is virtually overhead and has fainter stars nearby.

Once you have your eye in, you can start searching for deep-sky objects such as galaxies and nebulae. The Andromeda Galaxy (see p. 64) is a prime autumn target, which you can locate by taking a diagonal through the lower right star and the top left star of the Square of Pegasus, and carrying on the line as far again. It shows up as an oval blur, quite large, but don't expect to see the spiral structure that shows up in photos. Other easily found

A daily series of drawings of sunspots made by Michael Rosalina using 10 × 50 binoculars covered with solar filter material. The rotation of the Sun and small changes in the spots are evident.

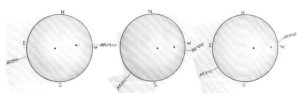

The Pleiades star cluster in Taurus as seen through 15 × 70 binoculars. The field of view of over four degrees makes the whole cluster and its surroundings visible, whereas a typical telescope field of view is less than a degree.

galaxies, though a lot smaller, are M81 and M82 (see pp. 21 and 83) in Ursa Major, best seen when they are high up in spring.

The Orion Nebula (see pp. 9 and 85) is a favourite target with binocular users, visible during the winter months into early spring. In summer, seek out the Lagoon Nebula (see pp. 45 and 84) in Sagittarius, and just sweep along the Milky Way to find numerous star clusters as well as heart-stopping views of the Milky Way itself, with its thousands of faint stars filling the field of view.

If you can hold the binoculars steady, you can make your own drawings of deep-sky objects – a skill which will stand you in good stead should you decide to progress to a telescope. It may seem quaint to do this when it's so easy to take photos through smartphones, but these objects are too faint to be photographed in this way. Making drawings of what you see actually helps you to see more detail by forcing you to look more carefully and for longer. And you will soon accumulate

a collection of observations that you can refer back to as your skills improve.

Star colours show up particularly well in binoculars. They are not vivid, but you can pick out the reddish colours of red giants and the bluish tints of hot young stars. However, if you're expecting the nebulae to show the spectacular hues that you see in photos, you'll be disappointed. Our eyes are just not sensitive enough to see the colours, apart from a few of what are termed planetary nebulae, which show up strongly blue, but these are mostly too small to be seen easily with binoculars.

There is one class of celestial objects where binoculars come into their own – comets. Every year or two we get a new comet which is easily visible with binoculars. Most are faint and unimpressive, but from time to time one appears that sports a tail and is well worth observing, even though it's not visible with the naked eye.

Every stargazer hopes that a really bright comet is about to burst into our skies, and when it does, binoculars will be the instrument of choice, with their good light grasp and comparatively wide field of view. So get those binoculars out – you never know what could be around the astronomical corner.

Mike Hezzlewood made this drawing of the Andromeda Galaxy from Burnley in Lancashire using 15 × 70 binoculars. Even its two smaller companion galaxies, M32 and M110, are visible.

CHOOSING & USING BINOCULARS　　89

Our view of the stars – a source of infinite amazement for scientists, stargazers and the millions of us who seek out rural places to rest and recuperate – is obscured by light pollution. It's a sad fact that many people may never see the Milky Way, our own Galaxy, because of the impact of artificial light.

LIGHT POLLUTION

Light pollution is a generic term referring to artificial light that shines where it is neither wanted nor needed. In broad terms, there are three types of light pollution:

- **Skyglow** – the pink or orange glow we see for miles around towns and cities, spreading deep into the countryside, caused by a scattering of artificial light by airborne dust and water droplets.
- **Glare** – the uncomfortable brightness of a light source.
- **Light intrusion** – light spilling beyond the boundary of the property on which a light is located, sometimes shining through windows and curtains.

CPRE, the countryside charity, has long fought for the protection and improvement of dark skies, and against the spread of unnecessary artificial light. CPRE commissioned LUC to create new maps of Great Britain's light pollution and dark skies to give an accurate picture of how much light is spilling up into the night sky and show where urgent action is needed. CPRE also sought to find where the darkest skies are, so that they can be protected and improved.

MAPPING

The maps are based on data gathered by the National Oceanographic and Atmospheric Administration (NOAA) in America, using the Suomi NPP weather satellite. One of the instruments on board the satellite is the Visible Infrared Imaging Radiometer Suite (VIIRS), which captures visible and infrared imagery to monitor and measure processes on Earth, including the amount of light spilling up into the night sky. This light is captured by a day/night band sensor.

The mapping used data gathered in September 2015, and is made up of a composite of nightly images taken that month as the satellite passed over the UK at 1.30 am.

The data was split into nine categories to distinguish between different light levels. Colours were assigned to each category, ranging from darkest to brightest, as shown in the chart below. The maps

Colour bandings to show levels of brightness

Categories	Brightness values (in nw/cm²/sr)*
Colour band 1 (darkest)	<0.25
Colour band 2	0.25–0.5
Colour band 3	0.5–1
Colour band 4	1–2
Colour band 5	2–4
Colour band 6	4–8
Colour band 7	8–16
Colour band 8	16–32
Colour band 9 (brightest)	>32

*The brightness values are measured in nanowatts/cm²/steradian (nw/cm²/sr). In simple terms, this calculates how the satellite instruments measure the light on the ground, taking account of the distance between the two.

are divided into pixels, 400 metres × 400 metres, to show the amount of light shining up into the night sky from that area. This is measured by the satellite in nanowatts, which is then used to create a measure of night-time brightness.

The nine colour bands were applied to a national map of Great Britain (see the following pages), which clearly identifies the main concentrations of night-time lights, creating light pollution that spills up into the sky.

The highest levels of light pollution are around towns and cities, with the highest densities around London, Leeds, Manchester, Liverpool, Birmingham and Newcastle. Heavily lit transport infrastructure, such as major roads, ports and airports, also show up clearly on the map. The national map also shows that there are many areas that have very little light pollution, where people can expect to see a truly dark night sky.

The results show that only 21.7 per cent of England has pristine night skies, completely free from light pollution (see the chart below). This compares with almost 57 per cent of Wales and 77 per cent of Scotland. When the two darkest categories are combined, 49 per cent of England can be considered dark, compared with almost 75 per cent in Wales and 87.5 per cent in Scotland. There are noticeably higher levels of light pollution in England in all the categories, compared with Wales and Scotland. The amount of the most severe light pollution is five times higher in England than in Scotland and six times higher than in Wales.

The different levels of light pollution are linked to the varying population densities of the three countries: where there are higher population densities, there are higher levels of light pollution. For example, the Welsh Valleys are clearly shown by the fingers of light pollution spreading north from Newport, Cardiff, Bridgend and Swansea. In Scotland, the main populated areas stretching from Edinburgh to Glasgow show almost unbroken levels of light pollution, creeping out from the cities and towns to blur any distinction between urban and rural areas.

Light levels in England, Wales and Scotland

Categories	England	Wales	Scotland	GB
Colour band 1 (darkest)	21.7%	56.9%	76.8%	46.2%
Colour band 2	27.3%	18.0%	10.7%	20.1%
Colour band 3	19.1%	9.3%	4.6%	12.6%
Colour band 4	11.0%	5.8%	2.8%	7.3%
Colour band 5	6.8%	3.8%	1.7%	4.6%
Colour band 6	5.0%	2.9%	1.2%	3.3%
Colour band 7	4.3%	2.1%	1.0%	2.8%
Colour band 8	3.2%	1.0%	0.9%	2.1%
Colour band 9 (brightest)	1.6%	0.2%	0.3%	1.0%

Adapted from Night Blight: Mapping England's light pollution and dark skies *CPRE (2016), with kind permission from CPRE. To see the full report and dedicated website, go to http://nightblight.cpre.org.uk/*

MAP OF BRITAIN'S LIGHT POLLUTION AND DARK SKIES
COURTESY OF CPRE/LUC

DARK SKIES & LIGHT POLLUTION

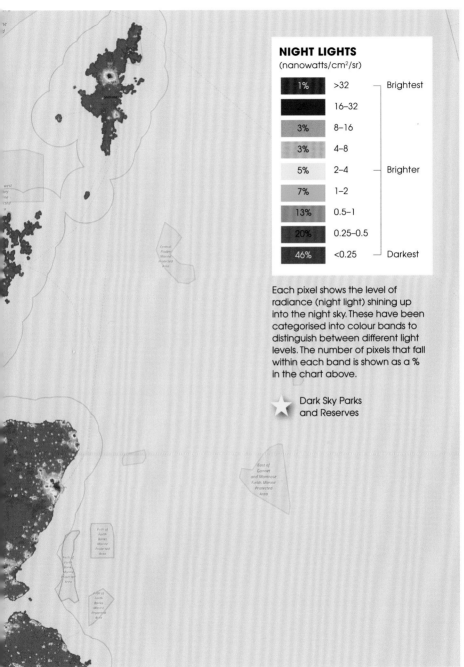

NIGHT LIGHTS
(nanowatts/cm²/sr)

%	Range	
1%	>32	Brightest
2%	16–32	
3%	8–16	
3%	4–8	
5%	2–4	Brighter
7%	1–2	
13%	0.5–1	
20%	0.25–0.5	
46%	<0.25	Darkest

Each pixel shows the level of radiance (night light) shining up into the night sky. These have been categorised into colour bands to distinguish between different light levels. The number of pixels that fall within each band is shown as a % in the chart above.

★ Dark Sky Parks and Reserves

Central Fladen Marine Protected Area

East of Gannet and Montrose Fields Marine Protected Area

Firth of Forth Banks Marine Protected Area

Firth of Forth Marine Protected Area

Firth of Forth Banks Marine Protected Area

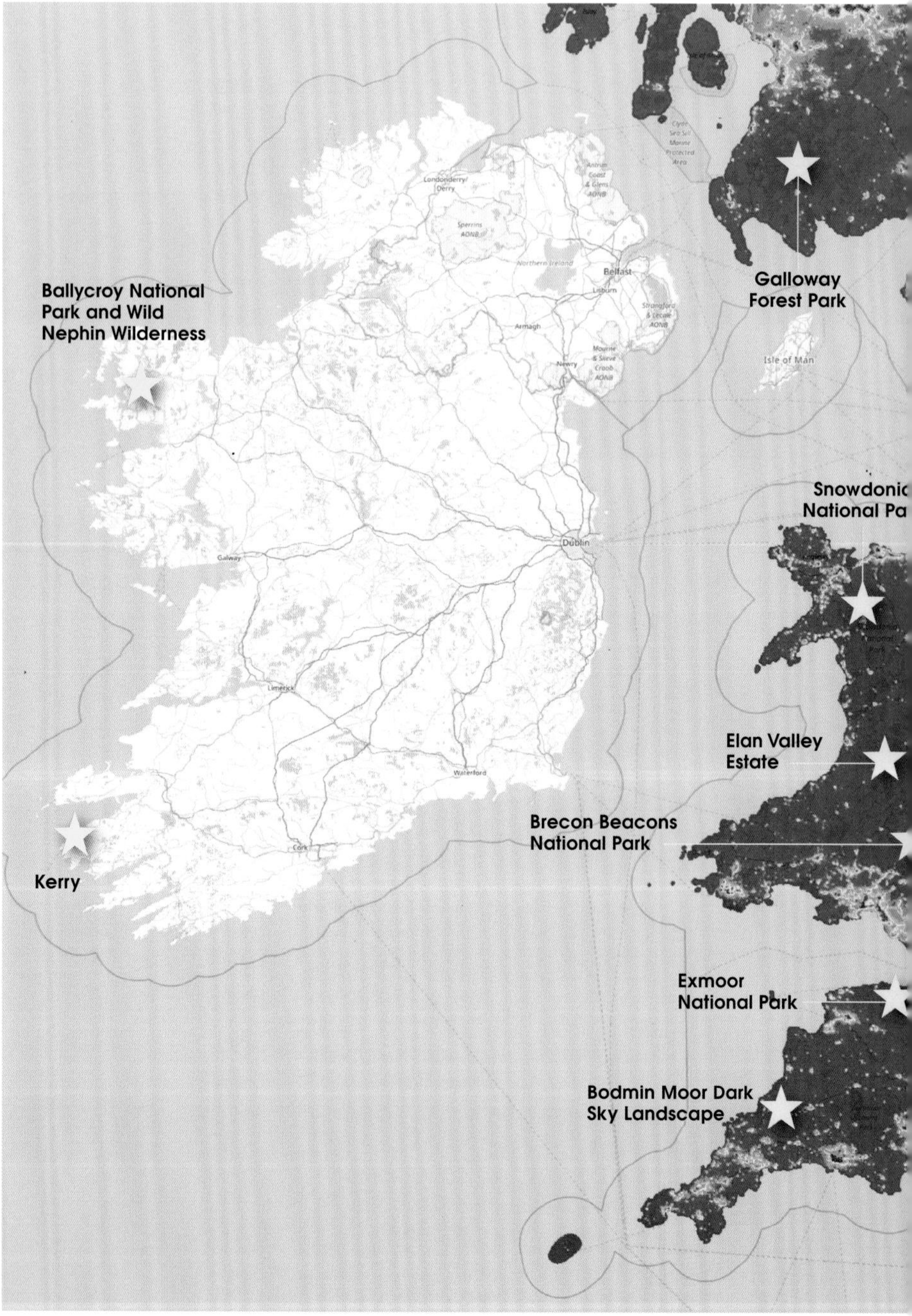
Ballycroy National Park and Wild Nephin Wilderness
Kerry
Galloway Forest Park
Snowdonia National Pa
Elan Valley Estate
Brecon Beacons National Park
Exmoor National Park
Bodmin Moor Dark Sky Landscape
Londonderry/Derry
Sperrins AONB
Northern Ireland
Belfast
Lisburn
Armagh
Newry
Dublin
Galway
Limerick
Waterford
Cork
Isle of Man

Moffat

Northumberland National
Park and Kielder Water
and Forest Park

★ Dark Sky Parks
and Reserves

Moore's Reserve
(South Downs)

THE AUTHORS

Professor **Heather Couper** was President of the British Astronomical Association, a Fellow of the Institute of Physics and a Fellow of the Royal Astronomical Society. She was awarded the CBE in 2007 for Services to Science. Heather sadly passed away in February 2020, while writing *Stargazing 2021*.

After researching at Cambridge, Professor **Nigel Henbest** became consultant to both *New Scientist* magazine and the Royal Greenwich Observatory. He is a future astronaut with Virgin Galactic.

Recognised internationally as writers and broadcasters on astronomy and space, Heather and Nigel have penned 50 books and more than 1000 articles in newspapers and magazines, as well as co-founding an international TV production company which clocked up 600 hours of factual programmes.

ACKNOWLEDGEMENTS

PHOTOGRAPHS
Front cover: Sara Wager, Horsehead nebula. **John Bell:** 29; **Nick Bull:** 59; **Dr J M Dean FRAS:** 11; **Andy Green:** 1; **James Harrop:** 35; **Nick Hart:** 85; **Nigel Henbest:** 7, 40, 96; **Michael Hezzlewood:** 89 (bottom); **ImagineChina/Alamy Stock Photo:** 12; **Peter Jenkins:** 23; **Pete Lawrence:** 47; **Mary McIntyre:** 71; **NASA:**/Carnegie Institution of Washington 31; /Jerry Lodigruss (Catching the Light) 60; /JPL-Caltech 18, 61; /NSS-DCA 13, 43; /Robert Gendler 84 (top); /UCLA 2–3; /VegaStar Carpentier 83; **Damian Peach:** 52; **Michael Rosalina:** 88 (bottom); **Robin Scagell:** 6, 84 (bottom), 86, 87, 88 (top), 89 (top); **Sara Wager:** 17; **Wikimedia:**/Anton Fernandez-Sanchez 19; /David Moug 48; /Brocken Inaglory 66; **Pete Williamson FRAS:** 65, 77.

ARTWORKS
Star maps: Wil Tirion/Philip's with extra annotation by Philip's.
Planet event charts: Nigel Henbest/Stellarium (www.stellarium.org).
pp. 80–82: Chris Bell.
pp. 90–95: Adapted from *Night Blight: Mapping England's light pollution and dark skies* CPRE (2016), with kind permission from CPRE.
To see the full report and dedicated website, go to http://nightblight.cpre.org.uk/
Maps © OpenStreetMap contributors, Earth Observation Group, NOAA National Geophysical Data Center. Developed by CPRE and LUC.